WEIDENFELD QUIZ BOOKS

John Julius Norwich

History Quiz

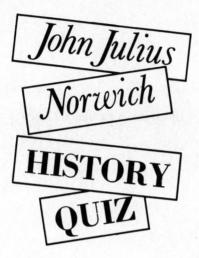

John Julius

Norwich

HISTORY

QUIZ

WEIDENFELD AND NICOLSON   LONDON

Illustrations by Simon Gooch

Copyright © John Julius Norwich 1983
Illustrations Copyright © Simon Gooch 1983

First published in Great Britain in 1983 by
George Weidenfeld & Nicolson Ltd
91 Clapham High Street
London SW4 7TA

ISBN 0 297 78279 7

Photoset by Deltatype, Ellesmere Port
Printed in Great Britain by
Butler & Tanner Ltd., Frome and London

Contents

Quizzes

Answers 89

'How', asked the authors of *1066 And All That* in one of their Test Papers, 'can you be so numb and vague about Arabella Stuart?' The question was unanswerable, the premise all too true. Nor, for most of us, are such feelings confined to the unfortunate Lady Arabella.

Yet the history of these islands is mercifully illuminated, time and time again, by little pools of light – generated by people or events that have for one reason or another become unforgettable and, while remaining firmly implanted in fact, have contrived also to pass into legend. It is with these pools, above all, that the following three hundred questions are concerned – not with the day-to-day fabric of history but with its occasional explosions: of greatness or glory, disgrace or disaster, comedy or crime.

This book is not, therefore, to be taken too seriously. It's a quiz, remember, not an examination; its purpose is not to instruct, merely to amuse. Of course you may pick up a few stray (and almost certainly useless) pieces of knowledge along the way, but they will be incidental. And I can promise you one thing: about Lady Arabella Stuart, you will remain every bit as numb and vague as you were before.

JOHN JULIUS NORWICH

Quizzes

From the Horse's Mouth

It's a marvellous moment when, reading history, you suddenly come across a piece of direct speech. For a moment the historian fades into the background and leaves you face to face with his subject – who, at that same moment, comes alive as never before. Of course all reported quotations are not accurate, or even authentic – how could they be? But some, one feels, could not have been made up, and others simply ring so true that one has to accept them.

Who said, of what:
a 'The lights are going out all over Europe.'?
b 'The Suez Canal has been flowing through my drawing-room'?

2 Which queen said: 'So *that's* what hay looks like'?

3 Which king is reported to have said:
a 'Harris, I am not well; pray get me a glass of brandy'?
b '*Non, j'aurai des maîtresses*'?
c 'I hate all Boets and Bainters'?

4 Who wrote in her last letter:
'Patriotism is not enough. I must have no hatred or bitterness towards anyone'?

11

Answers on page 89

5 What was the importance in the Second World War of the following lines of Verlaine? 'Les sanglots longs/Des violons/Bercent mon coeur/D'une langueur/Monotone.'

6 Who said, or wrote, and on what occasion:
  a 'I beseech you, in the bowels of Christ, think it possible you are mistaken'?
  b 'By God, Mr Chairman, at this moment I stand astonished at my own moderation!'?
  c 'Great God! This is an awful place'?

7 Who wrote:
  a 'History is more or less bunk'?
  b 'History a distillation of rumour'?
  c 'It takes a great deal of history to produce a little literature'?
  d 'War makes rattling good history; but peace is poor reading'?

8 What incident in history was described by the epigram?
>   Lord Chatham, with his sword undrawn,
>   Is waiting for Sir Richard Strachan;
>   Sir Richard, longing to be at 'em,
>   Is waiting for the Earl of Chatham.

9
>   Most Gracious Queen, we thee implore
>   To go away and sin no more;
>   But if that effort be too great,
>   To go away at any rate.
> Which queen is here addressed?

10 She was fat, ill-shaped, disfigured by the

small-pox, and short, while the prince was deformed. The princess had leave to refuse him, but replied that she would marry him if he were a baboon. 'Well then,' said the king, 'there is baboon enough for you.'

To which king, princess and prince does this quotation from the *Dictionary of National Biography* refer?

Oddly Enough

The British have always been a nation of eccentrics, and their eccentricity has often been reflected in their history. All of the following were curious in one way or another. But how?

What was unusual about:

1 The hand of Anne Boleyn?

2 The nose of Sir William Davenant?

3 The ear of Robert Jenkins?

4 The heart of Mary Tudor?

5 The coronation of Henry VI?

6 The coronation of George IV?

7 The travels of Berengaria of Navarre, Queen of Richard I?

8 The past of Eleanor of Aquitaine, Queen of Henry II?

9 September 1752?

10 The signing of the Armistice in 1918?

Answers on page 90

The Death of Kings

For God's sake, let us sit upon the ground
And tell sad stories of the death of kings:
How some have been depos'd, some slain
    in war,
Some haunted by the ghosts they have
    depos'd,
Some poison'd by their wives, some sleep-
    ing kill'd;
All murder'd: for within the hollow crown
That rounds the mortal temples of a king
Keeps Death his court. . . .

In English history, thank goodness, the record has not been quite as bad as this; most of our monarchs have died peacefully in their beds. But not all – and several of our royal deaths, even if not actually violent, have been at least unusual. Surrender now to the morbid streak that lurks in all of us, and see if you can answer the following:

1 To whom did Shakespeare give the words quoted above?

2 Whose death was caused by:
  a a red-hot poker?
  b a bolt from a crossbow?
  c pillows?

3 Which two monarchs since the Norman Conquest died without being crowned?

Answers on page 91

4 What were the last words of:
  a Charles I?
  b Charles II?
  c George V?

5 *a* Which monarch, although actually dying in bed, did so only after refusing to go to bed for fear of 'never rising again'?
  b Which monarch died in the presence of the German Emperor?

6 Which English king's sons are referred to in a medieval French rhyme which might be translated: 'Henry the fairest, shall die at Martel; Richard the Poitevin, shall die in the Limousin; John shall die, a landless King, in a litter'?

7 Which king's death provoked this response from the next day's *Times*? 'What eye has wept for him? What heart has heaved one throb of unmercenary sorrow?'

8 The third wife of one king, she died giving birth to another. Who are the people concerned?

9 Which king was told that he would die in Jerusalem, and – in a way – did so?

10 Which was the last king of England to die in battle?

Not Upon Oath . . .

'In lapidary inscriptions', as Dr Johnson pointed out, 'a man is not upon oath'; and the trouble about writing history – or reading it, for that matter – is that we always have to rely on what other people say. Sometimes they give us a wonderful portrait, but is it a true one? How far do we have to take the character of the portraitist into consideration? Who, for example, said this of whom?

1   Alas! whom shall men trust? I promise you I see no such thing as hath been shown me of her by picture or report. I am ashamed that men have praised her as they have done, and I like her not.

2   This monarch was famous only for his Beauty and his courage, of which the Picture we have here given of him, and his undaunted Behaviour in marrying one Woman while engaged to another, are sufficient proofs.

3   He was one of the most luminous, eloquent blunderers with which any people was ever afflicted. For fifteen years I have found my income dwindling away under his eloquence, and regularly in every session of parliament he has charmed every classical feeling and stripped me of every guinea I possessed. At the close of each brilliant display, an expedition failed

17

Answers on page 92

or a Kingdom fell. By the time his style had gained the summit of perfection, Europe was degraded to the lowest abyss of misery. God send us a stammerer; a tongueless man.

4 'If poor Tom had lived, I should have starved.'

5 'If he fell into the Thames it would be a misfortune; but if someone pulled him out, it would be a calamity.'

6 'His smile was like the silver plate on a coffin.'

7 If all the pictures and patterns of a merciless Prince were lost in the world, they might all again be painted to the life, out of the story of this King.

8 His awkward figure, his rolling eye, his rickety walk, his nervous tremblings, his slobbering mouth, his broad Scotch accent. . . .

9 —— was a saint-like thief, who, under the double cloak of religion and patriotism, committed a burglary in the constitution, and robbed the people of their title to liberty.

10 The literary loss is infinite . . . . —— was a pure modernist – a leader of the steam-and-whistle party *par excellence* and he had no understanding of any power of antiquity except a sort of jackdaw sentiment for cathedral towers. He knew nothing of nobler power of superstition – was essentially a stage manager and used everything for effect on the pit. His Christmas meant mistletoe and pudding – neither resurrection from dead, nor rising of new stars, nor teaching of wise men, nor shepherds. His hero is essentially the ironmaster.

The Missing Link

'Only connect', advised E. M. Forster; and indeed there are no two things so unrelated that some sort of connection between them cannot be found. But in the following groups there are *real* connections – it's not enough, for example, to say that the three gentlemen in No. 1 all begin with C! Here, then, are ten groups of pearls; all you have to do is thread them.

What have the following in common:

1 Clive, Castlereagh, Chatterton?

2 A Whig politician, an early Quaker, a martyrologist?

3 William II, Edward V, Edward VI?

4 Wat Tyler, Thomas Wyatt, Jack Cade?

5 Branodunum, Othona, Regulbium, Portus Adurni?

6 George V, Kaiser Wilhelm II, Queen Marie of Roumania, Alix Empress of Russia?

7 Richard, King of the Romans; Pope Adrian IV; the Empress Frederick of Prussia?

8 *a* St Stephen; St Swithun; St Vedast; St Bride?
   b St George; St Alphege; St Mary?

Gunpowder, Treason and Plot

Although we British are a peaceable enough people on the whole, our history sometimes seems to be an endless series of conspiracies of one kind or another. What is more, we apparently enjoy them. Has any other nation elevated a particularly nasty one into an excuse for annual public rejoicing?

1 What was the object of the following plots, and when – to a decade – did they take place?
   a Popish
   b Gunpowder
   c Rye House

2 A former British consul-general landed secretly in Ireland from a German submarine in 1916, to be executed four months later. Who was he, and why was he executed?

3 What were:
   a the Zinoviev Letter?
   b the Casket Letters?

4 Which is the odd man out and why? – Ridolfi, Masham, Babington, Throckmorton.

5 What was the name of the plan by Nazi

Germany to flood the world with forged British banknotes?

6 *a* Who, having led a revolt against William the Conqueror in 1070–1, was besieged by the King on the Isle of Ely?

  b Who, in 1403, rose against Henry IV in a rebellion in which his son and namesake died? (He himself died five years later in the battle of Bramham Moor.)

  c Who led a rebellion against James II in which he landed at Lyme Regis but was crushed at the battle of Sedgemoor in 1685?

7 Who, having been crowned as Edward VI in Dublin in 1487, ended his days turning a spit in the kitchen of Henry VII?

8 What Roman senator gave his name to a London street and what is its connection with a ministerial dinner party?

9 Of what is this a contemporary description?
  Just before sun-rising Mr Christian, with the master-at-arms, gunner's mate, and Thomas Birkett, seaman, came into my cabin while I was asleep, and seizing me, tied my hands with a cord behind my back and threatened me with instant death, if I spoke or made the least noise.

10 What was the name of a series of risings against Henry VIII in 1536–7 and who was its leader?

Any Other Name

A rose by any other name may well smell as sweet; but not all those characters referred to below were roses, or by any means fragrant. The fact remains that nicknames of one kind or another – affectionate, insulting, laudatory, or occasionally deliberately deceptive – are part and parcel of history.

1 Which kings were known as the following:
   a Beauclerk?
   b Lackland?
   c Rufus?
   d Old Rowley?
   e The Sailor King?
   f The Bastard?
   g Curtmantle?
   h Longshanks?

2 Who wrote to each other as Mrs Morley and Mrs Freeman?

3 Who were the Old Contemptibles, and why were they so called?

4 Who were:
   a The Hammer of the Scots?
   b The Hammer of the English?

5 Who used the following names and for what purposes?
   a Former Naval Person
   b David Winter

c Colonel Kent

6 Which monarch gave her close friends the following nicknames: 'Eyes', 'Spirit', 'Lids', 'Frog'? Who were the friends?

7 Which prominent figures in the Second World War were known as:
a Pug?
b Dickie?
c The Prof?
d Jumbo?
e The Auk?

8 Who were:
a The Fair Maid of Kent?
b The Maid of Norway?
c The Maid of Orleans?

9 Who were known as:
a Steenie?
b Starvation?
c Turnip?
d Tumbledown Dick?

10 What were the following Operations?
a Dynamo
b Sealion
c Overlord

Out of Wedlock

From the days of the Trojan War, sex has been a decisive factor in history; and although, as a consequence of their hormonal activity, the British can look back on nothing quite so dramatic as that, they can hardly, over the centuries, be described as slouches. Historical gossip-mongers – of whom I am one – should have little trouble with the following:

1 Of which kings or queens were the following the lovers or mistresses?
   a Jane Shore
   b Alice Perrers
   c Madame de Kielmannsegge (later Countess of Darlington)
   d Thomas Culpeper
   e Alice Keppel
   f Louise de Kéroualle
   g Amelia von Walmoden

2 Which king, by the time of his accession, had lived for some twenty years with a famous actress, who bore him no less than ten children? What was the name of the actress, and the surname given to the children?

3 Of which royal mistress was it written:

Here Rose the graced, not Rose the chaste,
    reposes:
The smell that rises is no smell of roses.
Who was her lover?

4 An English king once appointed his lover Regent of the Kingdom while he was abroad getting married. Who was the king, and who the lover?

5 Name four existing Dukedoms which are the direct or indirect result of the *amours* of Charles II – and the mistresses concerned?

6 Her real name was Emma Elizabeth Crouch. Her father wrote the popular Irish ballad 'Kathleen Mavourneen'. Settling in France, she became the greatest *demi-mondaine* of the Second Empire. On the outbreak of war in 1870 she converted her house into a hospital and spent 25,000 francs on the care of the wounded. Her nickname was '*La Lune Rousse*'. She died in poverty in 1886. Who was she?

7 She started as Evans, she ended as Cross, and her professional name was something else again. Had she married the man with whom she lived in the closest intimacy for nearly a quarter of a century, what would her name have been?

8 With whom would you associate:
a Fanny Brawne?
b Claire Clairmont?
c Mary Godwin?

9 Irving's leading lady and James McNeill Whistler's architect produced a son later famous for his liaison with a dancer who was ultimately garrotted. Who were they?

10 Each of Britain's two Prime Ministers in the First World War is famous for one particular liaison. Of the ladies concerned, the first subsequently married one of the members of her lover's cabinet; the second, who had served the Prime Minister for thirty years as his secretary, later married him. Who are the four people referred to?

Art and Architecture

What British architect:
a Began life as a gardener at Chatsworth?
b Took up architecture only at the age of thirty-five, after a successful career as a playwright?
c First made his name as a designer and producer of court masques?
d Began life as an astronomer?

Who built or designed the following?
a The Protestant Cathedral, Liverpool
b Coventry Cathedral
c Truro Cathedral
d The National Theatre
e Marlborough House
f The National Gallery
g The Cenotaph
h The Natural History Museum, South Kensington
i The Pagoda, Kew Gardens

With what houses do you associate:
a Emma Hamilton and H. G. Wells?
b The Duke of Wellington?
c The Duke of Marlborough?
d Benjamin Disraeli?
e T. E. Lawrence?

Who painted:
a *Mr and Mrs Andrews?*

Answers on page 98

b Ramsgate Sands?
c The Painted Hall at Greenwich?
d Marriage à la Mode?
e Work?

5 With what English counties do you associate:
a Old Crome?
b John Constable?
c Francis Smith?
d John Carr?

6 Whose last words were: 'We are all going to Heaven, and Vandyke is of the company'?

7 Who wrote of the 'Cockney impudence' whereby a coxcomb could ask 200 guineas for flinging a pot of paint in the public's face? Of whom? And with what result?

8 What is the Wilton Diptych?

9 Who said: 'He who resolves never to ransack any mind but his own, will be soon reduced, from mere barrenness, to the poorest of all imitations; he will be obliged to imitate himself'?

10 A merchant banker in the eighteenth century, a distinguished archaeologist in the nineteenth and an art-dealer of repute in the twentieth have been the three greatest benefactors to the National Gallery. Who were they?

The Black, the Bloody and the Rest

Nicknames again, but in a rather different form. In a way they provide a sort of historical shorthand; they certainly make the writing of history – and its reading – a good deal more colourful.

Identify:

a The Black Douglas
b Black Monday
c The Black Rood of Scotland

a Bloody Sunday
b The Bloody Assizes
c Eric Blood-Axe

a Bunker Hill
b Homildon Hill
c Halidon Hill

a The Gordon Riots
b The Rebecca Riots

a The Pensioner or Cavalier Parliament
b The Drunken Parliament
c The Long Parliament
d Barebones' Parliament

a Queen Anne's Bounty
b Queen Anne's Lace
c Queen Anne's Fan

Answers on page 99

7 *a* The Cat & Mouse Act
  b The 'Intolerable' Acts
  c The Five Mile Act

8 *a* Jack Ketch
  b Jack Straw
  c Jack Horner

9 *a* The Lady of England
  b The Lady of the Lake
  c The Lady of the Lamp

10 The CABAL

Dumb Friends

It is something of a commonplace to talk of the English love of animals, but none the less true for that. A surprising number of them have gone down into history – most of them, inevitably, horses and dogs, though one or two cats have made it as well. And there are thousands more in literature; but the White Rabbit, Nana and Mrs Tiggywinkle fall, alas, beyond the scope of our quiz. Do what you can with these:

What had Sorrel to do with a little gentleman in black velvet?

2 The Rat, the Cat and Lovell the Dog
Rule all England under the Hog.
Explain.

3 What were the names of the dogs of the following?
a Sir Isaac Newton
b Richard II
c Elizabeth Barrett Browning
d Charles Lamb

4 Who were:
a Hodge?
b Jumbo? (The first one)

5 Of whom are the following pub signs the badges?
a White Hart

33

 b Blue Boar
 c Bull's Head
 d Bear & Ragged Staff

6 Of whose animals are the following the obituaries?

 a God's humbler instrument, though meaner clay,
   Should share the glory of that glorious day.

 b Near this spot are deposited the remains of one who possessed Beauty without Vanity, Strength without Insolence, Courage without Ferocity, and all the Virtues of Man without his Vices. This praise, which would be unmeaning Flattery, if inscribed over human ashes, its but a just tribute to the memory of BOATSWAIN, a Dog.

7 Whose horse was awarded campaign medals by special order of Queen Victoria? What was the campaign and what was the name of the horse?

8 Whose horses were:
 a Black Agnes?
 b Black Bess?
 c Black Saladin?
 d White Surrey?
 e Roan Barbary?

9 I am His Highness's Dog at Kew:
 Pray tell me, Sir, whose Dog are you?
Who was H.H.? And who wrote the verse?

10 Who or what were: the Byerly Turk, the Darley Arabian and the Godolphin Barb?

The Great Wen

London – the subject is so vast that it could easily fill the whole book; my problem has not been thinking up the questions but trying to decide what to leave out. In choosing my final list I have included, I think, only one question – the second – that will give resident Londoners an advantage; for the rest, it should be level pegging for everyone.

1 Why was London built on its present site?

2 Where in London are the following statues, and who are the sculptors?
   a Lord Byron
   b Mrs Siddons
   c Boadicea
   d Florence Nightingale
   e Edward Jenner
   f General Gordon

3 After what or whom are the following streets named?
   a Downing Street
   b Jermyn Street
   c Lombard Street
   d Pall Mall
   e Piccadilly

Who said, or wrote, of the Great Fire of 1666:
   a 'A woman could piss it out'?
   b So I made myself ready presently, and walked to the Town and there got up

35

Answers on page 103

upon one of the high places, Sir J. Robinson's little son going up with me; and there I see the houses at that end of the bridge all on fire, and an infinite great fire on this and the other side the end of the bridge – which, among other people, did trouble me for poor little Michell and our Sarah on the Bridge?

5 What London church derives its shape from a foot-stool said to have been overturned by Queen Anne in order to show the architect (Thomas Archer) how she wanted it to look?

6 Who wrote the following?

   a   Forget six counties overhung with smoke,

       Forget the snorting steam and piston stroke. . .

       And dream of London, small and white and clean,

       The clear Thames bordered by its gardens green.

   b   Every blitz your resistance toughening

       From the Ritz to the Anchor and Crown–

       Nothing ever can override

       The Pride of London Town.

   c   But (when so sad thou canst not sadder)

       Cry; – and upon thy so sore loss

       Shall shine the traffic of Jacob's ladder

       Pitched betwixt Heaven and Charing Cross.

7 What, in nineteenth-century London, was:

   a a tosher?

b a bumper?
c a mudlark?

What London thoroughfare takes its name from an obscure battle fought in Calabria in 1806?

Who were the following famous – or infamous – Londoners?
a John Stow (1525–1605)
b Ned Ward (1688–1709)
c Thomas Cubitt (1788–1855)
d Kate Hamilton (mid-nineteenth century)

a Whose knowledge of London was 'extensive and peculiar'?
b What well-known quotation precedes the words: 'for there is in London all that life can afford'?

Murder Most Foul

Murder has always been the king of crimes – there are remarkably few detective stories about *theft* – and the British seem to have been rather good at it. This quiz covers a wide range of the most memorable examples, spanning a little over a thousand years. For amateurs of the genre, however, ten minutes should be ample for the solution of the questions below.

1 Who were the victims of:
  a Walter Tyrell?
  b John Felton?
  c John Bellingham?
  And where were they killed?

2 What group of people found themselves in particular danger in Whitechapel in 1888–9?

3 St Alphege, an Anglo-Saxon Archbishop of Canterbury, met his death by being bombarded with which of the following: (*a*) sticks (*b*) stones (*c*) books (*d*) bones?

4 What happened on 29 December 1170?

5 Which celebrated murderer:
  a First shot his seven victims, then drank their blood, then dissolved them in vats of sulphuric acid?
  b Set himself up as a doctor (and abortionist) at Rugeley, Staffordshire, and

poisoned not less than sixteen people before he was thirty, including his wife, his
brother, four of his legitimate children and
several of his fourteen illegitimate ones?

c Was a deacon in the Church of England,
and shot Margaret Reay, mistress of the
Earl of Sandwich, outside Covent Garden
Theatre in 1799?

Burke's the murderer, Hare's the thief,
And Knox the boy who buys the beef.
Can you explain this popular jingle?

7 What famous murders took place in:
a Branksome Chine, Bournemouth?
b 10, Rillington Place, London?
c The SS *Durban Castle?*

8 In what particular way did the case of
Hawley Harvey Crippen, who murdered his
wife in 1910 at 39, Hilldrop Crescent, London, make history?

9 Who was Peter the Painter, and what had he
to do with Winston Churchill?

10 What happened in Phoenix Park, Dublin, on
6 May 1882?

The Inner Man

One of the most encouraging aspects of history is the way in which food and drink have consistently improved over the centuries. In the Middle Ages, pepper and other spices were among the most important commodities; people would pay anything to disguise the taste of much of what they had to eat. Gluttony has always been one of the seven deadly sins, but nowadays we have, thank God, a good deal more to be gluttonous about.

1 What is the connection between:
  a Captain Cook and Sandwiches?
  b Henry VIII and Roast Beef?
  c William Pitt and Pork Pies?

2 What famous French chef offered his services to the British Army in the Crimean War and revolutionized Army catering?

3 Whose death was caused, or at least hastened, by:
  a A surfeit of lampreys?
  b Peaches and new cider?
  c A butt of malmsey?

4 To whom does the following verse refer and what does it mean?
  Brandy Nan, Brandy Nan, left in the lurch,
  Her face to the gin-shop, her back to the church.

Who were known as:

a the Cheesemongers?

b the Cherry-pickers?

What was Woolton pie, and after whom was it named?

Who was nicknamed 'Jeremy Twitcher' and why did he need to invent a familiar item of food?

Who wrote the following?

    The herbs were springing in the vale;
    Green ginger plants and liquorice pale
        And cloves their sweetness offered,
    With nutmegs too, to put in ale
    No matter whether fresh or stale
        Or else to be kept coffered.

Whom did Macaulay describe in the following passage:

    Being often very hungry when he sate down to his meals, he contracted a habit of eating with ravenous greediness. Even to the end of his life, and even at the tables of the great, the sight of food affected him as it affects wild beasts and birds of prey. . . . Whenever he was so fortunate to have near him a hare that had been kept too long, or a meat pie made of rancid butter, he gorged himself with such violence that his veins swelled and moisture broke out on his forehead.

10 What reason have we to be grateful to Thomas Garraway, a London coffee-house proprietor in the 1660s?

Odds and Ends

Not all questions can be filed neatly into categories, nor, perhaps, should they be. Here, then, is a ragbag: something, I hope, for everybody.

Why is Charing Cross so called?

What historical events might have been reported in the following news headlines?

a SENIOR CHURCHMAN BOOBS: CHAPLAIN CLAIMS NO PUN INTENDED

b WILLIAM STUMBLES: QUICK THINKING BY DUKE SAVES MORALE

c HAIL PRINCE NED! MOTHER AND SON DOING WELL, BUT KING'S BREAKDOWN SHOWS 'NO IMPROVEMENT'

d BRYDON THE BLESSED! SOLE SURVIVOR LIMPS HOME. QUEEN SENDS CONGRATULATIONS

What untoward event disrupted the Derby on 4 June 1913?

What events might have given rise to the following graffiti?

a EYETIES GO HOME

b READ BEDE

c MATILDA RULES OK

Where did the earliest recorded performance of *Hamlet* take place?

To what historical characters might these

43 Answers on page 107

advertisements have had particular appeal?

a GREENWICH DRY CLEANERS — SAME DAY SERVICE. CLOAKS A SPECIALITY

b DOES YOUR OVEN HAVE AN AUTOMATIC TIME SWITCH? JUST SET TO BAKING TIME REQUIRED — AND FORGET IT!

7 Can you give any historical references that might account for all or part of the following nursery rhymes?
   a 'Sing a Song of Sixpence'
   b 'Ring a Ring o' Roses'
   c 'Little Miss Muffet'

8 What was *Sphairistiké*, and why was it so called?

9 After the Scourers came the Nickers; after the Hawcubites, the Mohocks. Who were they?

10 Who was the first monarch to be buried in Westminster Abbey?

Eye-Witness

Some of the following passages are taken from letters, some from diaries, some from books, one from a poem. But they all have one thing in common: in each case the writer was personally involved as either a protagonist or an eye-witness. All you are asked to do is to identify the event or situation to which they refer; in certain questions, however, you should be able to identify the author as well.

1 The glimpse of the transept through the iron gates, the waving palms, flowers, statues, myriads of people filling the galleries and seats around, with the flourish of trumpets as we entered, gave us a sensation which I shall never forget, and I felt much moved. . . . It was and is a day to live forever.

2 When we came to the chapel of Henry the Seventh, all solemnity and decorum ceased; no order was observed, people sat or stood where they could or would; the yeomen of the guard were crying out for help, oppressed by the immense weight of the coffin; the Bishop read sadly, and blundered in the prayers; the fine chapter, *Man that is born of a Woman* was chanted, not read; and the anthem, besides being immeasurably tedious, would have served as well for a nuptial.

Answers on page 109

3   The barge approached, and ranged alongside. The first lieutenant came up the side, and to Maitland's eager and blunt question 'Have you got him?' he answered in the affirmative.

4   He nothing common did or mean
Upon that memorable scene
But, with a keener eye,
The axe's edge did try:

Nor called the Gods with vulgar spite
To vindicate this helpless Right
But bow'd his comely head
Down, as upon a bed.

5   . . . and David was thrown down the stairs from the Palace where he was slain, and brought to the Porter's lodge, who taking off his clothes said 'This was his destiny; for upon this chest was his first bed when he came to this place, and now he lieth a very niggard and misknown knave.'

6   When I had lain there some little time, I still had reflexion enough to suffer some uneasiness in the thought that I should be trampled upon when dead. . . . With some difficulty I raised myself and gained the platform a second time, where I presently lost all sensation. Of what passed in this interval to the time of my resurrection . . . I can give you no account.

7   Several charcoal fires being first made in his large study, he brought with him into that place his winding-sheet in his hand, and having put off all his clothes, had this sheet put on him, and so tied with knots at his head and feet, and his hands so placed as dead bodies are usually fitted to be shrowded and put into their coffin, or grave. Upon this urn he thus stood, with his eyes shut, and with so much of the sheet turned aside as might shew his lean, pale and deathlike face. . . .

8 The appearance of a monarch has something in it like the rising of a sun. There are indications which announce the luminary's approach; a streak of light – the tipping of a cloud – the singing of the lark – the brilliance of the sky, till the cloud edges get brighter and brighter and he rides majestically in the heavens. So with a king's advance. A whisper of mystery turns all eyes to the throne. Suddenly two or three rise; others fall back; some talk, direct, hurry, stand still, or disappear. Then three or four of high rank appear from behind the throne; an interval is left; the crowds scarcely breathe. Something rustles, and a being buried in satin, feathers and diamonds rolls gracefully into his seat. The room rises with a sort of feathered, silken thunder.

9 The writer of the following obituary knew the subject well.

He was debonair, easy of access, and not bloody or cruel. His countenance was fierce, and his voice great. He was proper of person, and every motion became him. He was a lover of the sea and skilful in shipping. . . . He loved planting and building, and brought in a politer way of living, which passed to luxury and intolerable expense. He had a particular talent in telling stories and facetious passages. . . . He took delight to have a number of little spaniels follow him and lie in his bedchamber, where oftentimes he suffered the bitches to puppy and give suck, which rendered it very offensive and indeed made the whole court nasty and stinking. An excellent prince, doubtless, had he been less addicted to women.

Who was the writer, and who the subject?

10 Honoured Fathre,

This comes to tell you that I am alive and hearty except three fingers; but that's not much, it might have been my head. I told brother Tom I should like to see a greatly battle, and I have seen one, and we have peppered the Combined rarely. . ; and for the matter of that, they fought us pretty tightish for French and Spanish. Three of our mess are killed, and four more of us winged. How my fingers got knocked overboard I don't know, but off they are, and I never missed them till I wanted them. You see, by my writing, it was my left hand, so I can write to you and fight for my King yet. We have taken a rare parcel of ships, but the wind is so rough we cannot bring them home, else I should roll in money, so we are busy smashing 'em, and blowing 'em up wholesale.

Once More Into the Breach

Battlewise, we in this country have got off very lightly. Just think of the vast fields of continental Europe, where invading armies have marched and countermarched for centuries. (Let us hope they have stopped at last – but we can never be sure.) In Britain, we can point to Hastings, a handful of sites dating from the Wars of the Roses and the Civil War, a few more along the borders and in Scotland, and one or two isolated curiosities like Sedgemoor. But none of these battles would count as more than petty skirmishes today. For most of this quiz, therefore, we shall be travelling abroad. But take heart: the places may be foreign but the history remains our own.

1 When did hostile foreign troops last set foot in Britain? What was their nationality and that of their leader?

2 In whose reign were these battles fought?
  a Poitiers
  b Culloden
  c Killicrankie
  d Flodden
  e Battle of the Standard
  f Evesham
  g Sedgemoor

3 Who said: 'I always say that, next to a battle lost, the greatest misery is a battle gained'?

4 Identify the following battles:

   a When Edward III defeated Philip VI of France in 1346, with great French losses. What new English weapon ensured this result?

   b When British and French troops fought side by side, a division of the French army having been brought into the battle by a fleet of 600 taxi-cabs.

   c A victory for the Jacobites in 1745 which briefly gave them control of Scotland.

5 Which of the following is a description of the Battle of Stanford Bridge?

   a When Harold lost to Harold who later defeated William

   b When two Williams fought a Harold who had just defeated another Harold

   c When two Harolds fought for a prize which later went to William

6 *a* Who was the last reigning British monarch to command his army in battle? Did he win?

   b Which future British monarch was present at the most important naval engagement of the First World War? And what was it?

   c Which future British Prime Minister wrote: 'I am glad to have added the experience of a cavalry charge to my military repertoire'?

7 What is, or was:

a Big Bertha?

b A doodle-bug?

c A Mulberry?

d Big Willy and Little Willy?

8 To what battles do the following lines refer? And who wrote them?

a He that shall live this day, and see old
  age,

  Will yearly on the vigil feast his neigh-
  bours,

  And say, 'Tomorrow is Saint Crispian.'

b The wretched, bloody, and usurping
  boar,

  That spoil't your summer fields, and
  fruitful vines,

  Swills your warm blood like wash, and
  makes his trough

  In your embowell'd bosoms, this foul
  swine

  Has now even in the centre of this
  isle. . . .

c 'And everybody praised the Duke
  Who this great fight did win.'
  'But what good came of it at last?'
  Quoth little Peterkin.
  'Why that I cannot tell', said he,
  'But 'twas a famous victory.'

d The thunder-clouds close o'er it, which
  when rent

  The earth is covered thick with other
  clay

  Which her own clay shall cover, heaped
  and pent

  Rider and horse – friend, foe – in one red

Burial blent.

e   Into the jaws of Death
        Into the mouth of Hell
        Rode the Six Hundred.

9 What naval battle was fought in December 1914 in the South Atlantic in which the British sank the *Scharnhorst*, the *Gneisenau*, the *Nürnberg* and the *Leipzig*?

10 Which battles were fought on:
  a 25 October, 1415?
  b 21 October, 1805?
  c 22 August, 1485?
  d 13 August, 1704?
  e 14 June, 1645?
  f 18 June, 1815?

Done to Death

Another grisly subject, I'm afraid; but executions have played a regrettably large part in English history and, for all their horror, have an undeniably dramatic value. English literature, too, would be poorer without them.

1 Who, feeling the edge of his executioner's axe said: ' 'Tis a sharp remedy, but a sure one for all ills'?

2 Which member of the House of Lords was found guilty – by his Peers, naturally – of murder, and was refused execution by beheading? The King is reported to have said, 'No, he has done the deed of the bad man, and he shall die the death of bad man.' (It has been said, however, that as a concession to his rank the rope to hang him was made of silk.)

3 Who was the last Peer of the Realm to be found guilty of high treason and publicly executed on Tower Hill?

4 What torture was introduced by Henry VIII in 1531 as a statutory punishment for poisoners?

5 Who wrote the following shortly before being executed?

a   Lord! since thou know'st where all these
      atoms are,
      I'm hopeful thou'll recover once my
      dust
      And confident thou'll raise me with the
      just.

b   My prime of youth is but a frost of cares,
      My feast of joy is but a dish of pain,
      My crop of corn is but a field of tares,
      And all my goodes is but vain hope of
      gain.
      The day is fled, and yet I saw no sun,
      And now I live, and now my life is done!

6 *a* Who went to her death accompanied by
      her Skye terrier?
   b How many of Henry VIII's wives were
      executed? And which?

7 Of whom did John Aubrey write the following?
      After he was beheaded, his trunke was
      interred in Chelsey church. . . . His head
      was upon London bridge. . . . One day as
      one of his daughters was passing under the
      Bridge, looking on her father's head, says
      she, That head haz layn many a time in
      my Lapp, would to God it would fall into
      my Lap as I passe under. She had her
      wish, and it did fall into her lappe, and is
      now preserved in a vault in the Cathedral
      Church at Canterbury.

8 Who wrote: 'I went out to Charing Cross, to
   see Major-General Harrison hanged, drawn
   and quartered; which was done there, he

looking as cheerful as any man could do in that condition.' And who was Harrison?

9 To which single place would you have gone had you wished to be sure of seeing James Maclaine, Claude Du Vall, and William Parsons?

10 On Monday 12 February 1554, Lady Jane Grey was beheaded on Tower Hill, having just been forced to witness the execution of her husband.
  a What was the charge?
  b For how long had she – theoretically – been Queen of England?
  c What was her claim to the throne?
  d How old was she at the time of her death?

Heads, you win...

The Printed Word

Without books there would be no history; but this quiz is not only about books of history, it is also about the history of books. Historians, bibliophiles, men of letters, step this way.

1 Which book was the subject of legislation in 1549, 1552, 1662 and 1980?

2 Who wrote the following early accounts of Britain (translated from the original Latin)?

a Goaded by such mutual encouragements, the whole island rose under the leadership of Boudicca, a lady of royal descent – for Britons make no distinction of sex in their leaders.

b This is how the present life of man on earth appears to me, O King, as compared with that time which is unknown to us: as if you, sitting at dinner with your earldormen and thegns in the wintertime. . . . A sparrow flies swiftly through the hall, entering through one door it soon goes out through the other. . . .

c All the Britons, indeed, dye themselves with woad, which produces a blue colour, and makes their appearance in battle more terrible. . . . Groups of ten or twelve men have wives together in common, and particularly brother along with brother, and father with sons.

3 Which famous British historians wrote the following opening lines to their most celebrated books?

a In the second century of the Christian Era, the empire of Rome comprehended the fairest part of the earth, and the most civilized portion of mankind. . . .

b In the summer of the Roman year 699, now described as the year 55 before the birth of Christ, the proconsul of Gaul, Gaius Julius Caesar, turned his gaze upon Britain. . . .

4 In which book does the following passage occur?

Edward III had very good manners. One day at a royal dance he noticed some men-about-court mocking a lady whose garter had come off, whereupon to put her at her ease he stopped the dance and made the memorable epitaph: '*Honi soie qui mal y pense*' ('Honey, your silk stocking's hanging down') and having replaced the garter with a romantic gesture gave the ill-mannered courtiers the Order of the Bath. (This was an extreme form of torture in the Middle Ages.)

5 To whom are Shakespeare's sonnets dedicated?

6 What was the first book to be printed in England?

7 Arrange the following in chronological order
   of publication?
   a Bunyan's *Pilgrim's Progress*
   b Hobbes's *Leviathan*
   c Burton's *Anatomy of Melancholy*
   d Browne's *Religio Medici*
   e Shakespeare's *The Tempest*

8 What is the Book of Kells, and what is its
   subject matter?

9 Sir Walter Raleigh completed only the first
   volume of his *History of the World*, (though it
   runs to 1,300 folio pages) which begins with
   the Creation and ends at 168 BC. In what
   circumstances was it written, and why was it
   banned by James I?

10 What was the *Eikon Basiliké*?

The Body Politic

For the first seven centuries since the Norman Conquest, English history was shaped principally by its reigning monarchs: for the last two, the major role has been assumed by Prime Minister and Parliament. Sometimes our leaders have been men of genius, sometimes they have been almost paralytically incapable; still, one way or another, we seem to have muddled through more successfully than most. The following questions mark, perhaps, a few milestones along the road.

1 *a* Who designed the present Palace of Westminster?

b Why was this new Palace necessary?

c In what year was the Chamber of the House of Commons destroyed by bombing?

d Where did Charles I hold his parliament during the Civil War?

2 These vital interests should render Great Britain the earnest and unyielding opponent of the Russian projects of annexation and aggrandisement. . . . Having come thus far on the way to universal empire is it probable that this gigantic, swollen power will pause in its career? The arrest of the Russian scheme of annexation is a matter of the highest moment. In this instance the

Answers on page 114

interest of democracy and of England go hand in hand.

Who wrote these words? (*a*) Winston Churchill (*b*) W. E. Gladstone (*c*) Lord Palmerston (*d*) Karl Marx

3 When, and why, does an MP apply for the Stewardship of the Chiltern Hundreds?

4 *a* Which two great Victorian Prime Ministers were related by marriage?

   b Which two recent Conservative Prime Ministers were related by marriage?

   c Which two Prime Ministers of Edward VII's reign were related by blood?

5 The 'Hawarden Kite' was which of the following?

   a The name given to the train that was especially hired to take sightseers down to Wales to watch Gladstone chop down trees

   b An interview – supposedly confidential – that was given by Gladstone's son Herbert in which he disclosed his father's conversion to Home Rule

   c Disraeli's celebrated term of abuse for Gladstone's Midlothian campaign of 1879

6 Three of the novels listed below were written by one British Prime Minister, the fourth by another. Who were the Prime Ministers, and who wrote which?

   a *Vivian Grey*

   b *Savrola*

c The Infernal Marriage
d Ixion in Heaven

7 Which English family has produced members of Parliament in the last four generations, the Christian name of the first being the same as the third, and that of the second being the same as the fourth?

8 In what order, chronologically, did the following events occur in England?
a Catholic Emancipation
b The First Reform Bill
c Emancipation of Slaves
d Abolition of Window Tax

9 In his *Areopagitica*, what great Englishman sounded a call for what fundamental liberty?

10 Who was the last Prime Minister to sit in the House of Lords?

A Chapter of Accidents

...and not only accidents either, but disasters, calamities, catastrophes of all kinds. History is so liberally peppered with them that one sometimes wonders how we manage to get on at all. . .

1 How did the following meet their deaths:
   a William I?
   b James Wyatt, architect?
   c William Huskisson, statesman?
   d William of Sens and George Basevi, architects?

2 To what financial disaster does this poem of Swift's relate:
   The nation then too late will find,
   Computing all their cost and trouble,
   Directors' promises but wind
   —— —— at best a mighty ——.

3 To which great nautical disaster do the following figures refer: First class – 63%, Second class – 42%, Third class – 25%?

4 What were the circumstances of the loss of the following ships:
   a The *Revenge*?
   b The *Hood*?
   c The *Mary Rose*?

d The *White Ship*?
e The *Prince of Wales* and the *Repulse*?

Of what event in April 1750 did Horace Walpole write?

> Turner, a great chinaman at the corner of the next street has a jar cracked by the shock; he originally asked ten guineas for the pair, he now asks twenty. . .

Who died after catching a cold while stuffing a hen with snow as an experiment in refrigeration?

What famous disaster occurred on 28 December 1879, just outside Dundee, causing the deaths of some seventy people, having been previously prophesied and being subsequently commemorated by the Scottish poet William McGonagall?

An aeroplane accident at Gibraltar on 4 July 1943, in which a prominent wartime leader was killed, was subsequently represented in a play by a German playwright as having been deliberately engineered by Sir Winston Churchill. Who was the leader, who was the playright, and what was the name of his play?

What unprecedented misfortune caused HMS *Victoria*, flagship of the Mediterranean fleet, to sink, in perfect weather, a few miles off the Lebanese coast on 22 June 1893?

On 4 October 1930 the Secretary of State for

Air, Lord Thompson, set off for Karachi. He never got there. In what was he travelling?

Glad Rags

History is one long fancy-dress parade. It is impossible to think of Henry VIII without his short skirt and stockings (with garter of course); of Elizabeth I without her high collar fanning out behind; of Victoria without her mourning bombazine. And clothes reflect, like nothing else perhaps, the spirit of the age – compare Cromwell's leather jerkin with the frills and furbelows of the Restoration, just a year or two later.

Which king put on two shirts on the last day of his life?

After whom are the following garments named?
a Top boots either covering the knee or ending just below it
b A knitted woollen over-waistcoat with or without sleeves
c An overcoat with no shoulder seam and sleeves extending to the neck

What is:
a a burgonet?
b an armet?
c a bascinet?

Which King of England always slept in woollen drawers, even on his wedding night?

Answers on page 116

5 What American champion of women's rights came to London in 1851 and gave her name to an article of clothing?

6 What is Spanish Bombast?

7 Who wrote the following? And who was the Queen?

14th. To the Privy Seale and there to my lord's where Dr Pin, the tailor, and I agreed upon his making me a velvet coat and cape, the first that ever I had.

22nd. This morning hearing that the Queen grows worse again, I went to stop the making of my velvet dress till I see whether she lives or dies.

8 What was a farthingale and when did it appear?

9 Which king was found to have jewelled gloves still on his hands when his coffin was opened at the end of the eighteenth century?

10 Who or what were Macaronis?

Dust To Dust

I once knew a man who, because of an unfortunate mistake by the Obituaries Editor of *The Times*, opened his paper one morning and read his own obituary notice. He was furious, not because of the mistake but because he thought the notice nowhere near good enough. How many of us, I wonder, would be genuinely satisfied by whatever is going to be said or written about us after we are dead? But this quiz isn't only about obituaries and epitaphs; it also seeks answers to that time-honoured question, more usually asked in another context: What became of the body?

The following Kings were all buried abroad. Where?

a William the Conqueror
b James II
c George I

In Poet's Corner in Westminster Abbey some memorials carry quotations from the poets commemorated. On whose can you read the following?

a   Time held me green and dying,
       Though I sang in my chains like the sea.

b   In the prison of his days
       Teach the free man how to praise.

c   The Communication of the dead is
       tongued with fire
       beyond the language of the living.

Answers on page 117

d   But there is that within me which shall tire
Torture and Time, and breath when I expire.

3   Here lies Fred
Who was alive and is dead:
Had it been his father,
I had much rather;
Had it been his brother,
Still better than another;
Had it been his sister
No one would have missed her;
Had it been the whole generation,
Still better for the Nation:
But since 'tis only Fred
Who was alive and is dead —
There's no more to be said.
Who was Fred? And who was his father?

4 Who was 'A very gallant gentleman'? And where is he so described?

5 Where is the earliest complete surviving monument in England of an English king? And whose is it?

6 Where would you find the grave of:
a Sir Francis Drake?
b Keats?
c Freud?
d Rupert Brooke?

7 The following all have unusual tombs or memorials. What form do they take?
a John Hanning Speke

b Sir Richard Burton

c Karl Marx

'O RARE ——' Who?

Whose are the following epitaphs?

a *Si monumentum requiris, circumspice*

b Lie heavy on him, Earth! for he
    Laid many heavy loads on thee.

c His foe was folly and his weapon wit

What famous tomb carries an inscription cursing anyone who should disturb the body beneath?

Servants of God

Religion, all over the world, has had an influence on history that it is impossible to exaggerate; and most of it, alas, has been harmful. The Crusades, the Wars of Religion, the Inquisition, the persecutions of Catholics, Protestants, Jews, Albigensians – the list could be extended indefinitely. In this country, too, we have suffered; but on the credit side we can be grateful, not only for the spiritual benefits conferred but also for much of our best art and architecture, literature and music, and for many of our best-loved customs and traditions.

1 What early Quaker walked barefoot into Lichfield, bewailing its misfortune?

2 Who or what were the following?
   a The Lollards
   b The Arminians
   c The New Connexion

3 Who said the following?
   a 'Had I but served God as diligently as I have served my King he would not have given me over in my gray hairs.'
   b 'Be of good comfort, Master Ridley, and play the man. We shall this day light such a candle by God's grace in England, as (I trust) shall never be put out.'
   c 'Sin is behovely, but all shall be well, and

all shall be well, and all manner of things shall be well.'

Which Baptist preacher spent twelve years in prison for refusing to cease public preaching (1660–72)? Where was the prison and what did he write there?

Attach the following hymns to their authors:
a 'Lead Kindly Light'
b 'Let us with a gladsome mind'
c 'O God our Help in Ages Past'
d 'He who would valiant be'
e 'Jesu lover of my soul'
f 'Rock of Ages'
g 'Jerusalem'
i   John Bunyan
ii   Charles Wesley
iii J. H. Newman
iv   John Milton
v   Isaac Watts
vi   William Blake
vii Augustus Toplady

How did the following martyrs meet their deaths?
a Thomas Cranmer
b Edmund Campion
c Margaret Clitherow

Which religious fanatic claimed that she was about to give birth to a new Messiah, and left a box which, opened 113 years after her death, was found to contain a woman's nightcap and a lottery ticket?

8 What are the following Bibles:
  a The Wicked Bible?
  b The Breeches Bible?
  c The Bug Bible?
  d The Leda Bible?
  e The Treacle Bible?

9   Sinne is where our Ladie sate
    Heaven turned is to hell,
  Sathan sittes where our Lord did swaye,
    Walsingham oh farewell.
What is the subject of these lines, and why
the lament?

10 Who were:
  a the Irvingites?
  b the Muggletonians?
  c the Peculiar People?

Psst . . . Have you heard?

At least twice in our century, a scandal has toppled a throne; most of them, however, are fortunately more like rocks dropped into a pool: a big splash, a few ripples, and then all is still again – except the pens of social historians. There were few scandals till the invention of newspapers, but there has been no shortage since: these questions cover only a small – though I hope representative – selection.

Where was 'Happy Valley' and what brought it into prominence?

What was the Tranby Croft Case?

Whose memoirs begin: 'I shall not say why and how I became, at the age of fifteen, the mistress of the Earl of Craven'?

In whose trial was the following letter brought up in evidence?
> My Own Boy,
> Your sonnet is quite lovely, and it is a marvel that those red rose-leaf lips of yours should have been made no less for music or song than for madness of kisses.

Who, in the later nineteenth century, did

Answers on page 120

Thomas Castro, a butcher of Wagga-Wagga, NSW, claim to be, and with what result?

6 For what, in the 1930s, did the Rev. Harold Davidson become notorious?

7 The daughter of an English peer, she went to Germany in 1934 and became besotted with Hitler. On the outbreak of war in 1939 she shot herself – not fatally – was returned to England, and died in Scotland in 1948. Who was she?

8 Which Victorian Cabinet Minister had his career blighted after being cited in a divorce case in 1885?

9 A Royal Duke, Commander-in-Chief of the Army, was the subject of a parliamentary enquiry after accusations that he had yielded to the influence of his mistress in the matter of military honours and promotions, she having accepted bribes from those concerned. He was found guilty of carelessness but not of corrupt practices. Who was he, who was the mistress, and where is his monument?

10 What actress (a protégée of Garrick, who offered her the role of Cordelia opposite his Lear) and poetess (she was later called 'The English Sappho') so captivated the future George IV that he wrote her a series of passionate love letters proposing marriage –

letters that the Palace subsequently had to
buy back for £5,000?

New Frontiers

'To myself I seem to have been only a boy playing on the sea-shore, and diverting myself in now and then finding a smoother pebble or a prettier shell than ordinary, whilst the great ocean of truth lay all undiscovered before me.' Those words are by Sir Isaac Newton – a most unpleasant man, but the first and arguably still the greatest of English scientists. Since his day we have made a good many inroads into the great ocean of truth; though how much of it remains still undiscovered is anybody's guess. A few of those who have struck out into it more bravely than most are the subjects of the questions below.

1 With what do you associate:
  a James Brindley?
  b John Harrison?
  c Dr John Collis Browne?
  d Frank Whittle?
  e Edward Jenner?

2 He first came to England as an oboist in the Hanover Guards Band; later he was organist at Bath Abbey, private astronomer to George III and discoverer of the planet Uranus. Who was he?

3 Who is generally held to be responsible for:
  a The Miners' Safety Lamp?
  b the perfecting of steam engines?

c the 'puddling process' for wrought iron?
d the hovercraft?
e the 'bouncing bomb'?

4 Who is said to have been described on his tombstone as 'Father of English Chemistry and brother to the Earl of Cork'?

5 Who was 'Blind Jack of Knaresborough' and what do we owe to him?

6 Which of the processes given here is held to be the invention of the following?
a John Kay: (i) The Spinning Mule, (ii) The Shuttling Jenny, (iii) the Flying Shuttle
b James Hargreaves: (i) The Shuttling Mule, (ii) The Flying Spinner, (iii) The Spinning Jenny

7 Who was the 'Railway King' and why was he so called?

8 With what or with whom do you connect the following ships, and what was the purpose of their voyages?
a The *Bounty*
b The *Endeavour*
c The *Beagle*
d The *Terra Nova*
e The *Erebus* and the *Terror*
f The *Endurance*

9 Who discovered what he called 'dephlogisticated air' and what was it?

10 What was the Birmingham Lunar Society?

The White Man's Burden

'Everything that's red' – I can hear my nanny saying it now, as she pointed to an enormous terrestrial globe that was slowly revolving outside Selfridge's as part of the Christmas decorations – 'belongs to England.' Most of those countries, curiously enough, still tend to be coloured red on maps, but there's precious little that remains ours. People will argue for ever whether the Empire was a good or a bad thing; but it was certainly an exciting chapter in our history, and it deserves a quiz of its own.

1 With which empire-builders do you associate:
a Sarawak?
b Singapore?
c Zambia and Zimbabwe?
d Nigeria?

2 What were the former (imperial) names of:
a Malawi?
b Botswana?
c Tanzania?
d Ghana?

3 Who said 'The key of India is not Herat or Kandahar. The key of India is London'?

4 Where would you find Tipu's Tiger? And what is it?

5 To what was Sydney Smith referring when he wrote: 'The ancient profession of picking pockets will certainly not become more discreditable from the knowledge that it may eventually lead to the possession of a farm of a thousand acres on the river Hawkesbury'?

6 Of what did Palmerston say that its functions should be to strip the local quadrupeds of their furs and keep the local bipeds off their liquor?

7 Who is said to have inspired W. S. Gilbert to write the song 'I am the very model of a modern major-general' in *The Pirates of Penzance*, and by what military expression is he remembered?

8 'It is settled,' said Disraeli to Queen Victoria, 'You have it, Madam.' What did she have?

9   Too late! Too late to save him,
    In vain, in vain they tried;
    His life was England's glory,
    His death was England's pride.
  Who is the subject of this verse?

10 Who wrote a cheque for Five Million, Three Hundred and Thirty-Eight Thousand, Six Hundred and Fifty-Eight Pounds and for what?

Spare Rib

The female of the species – or at least of *our* species – is not, thank God, more deadly than the male; but she certainly pulls her weight. From the distaff side (and what a misnomer *that* has come to be) have come three of our greatest sovereigns, even if Bloody Mary did let the side down a bit; and, I suspect, one of our greatest Prime Ministers. It's a pity that modern feminists have got so chippy; still, I expect they'll get over it.

1 Who sounded 'the First Blast of the Trumpet against the Monstrous Regiment of Women'?

2 *a* Who was the first woman to take her seat as a member of Parliament?
  b Who was the first person in England to set up a hospital intended for and entirely staffed by women?

3 Who said: 'The strongest will be wanted at the washtub'?

4 For what deeds of courage were the following known:
  a Grace Darling?
  b Edith Cavell?
  c Odette Churchill?

5 What niece of an English Prime Minister

went through a form of coronation among the ruins of Palmyra?

6 What family included the following members, and what was the relationship between them:

a Augusta, Augusta Ada, Annabella, Allegra?

b Charlotte, Emily, Anne?

c Sylvia, Emmeline, Christabel, Adela?

7 Which British composer and writer went to prison for her suffragette beliefs and was there seen conducting her *March of the Women* out of a prison window with a toothbrush?

8 a Which three queen consorts were called Elizabeth?

b Which five queen consorts were called Anne (or Ann)?

c Which five queen consorts (since the Norman Conquest) were called Catherine (or Katherine)?

And to whom were they married?

9 Who were 'The Queen's Four Marys'?

10 The mother wrote *Thoughts on the Education of Daughters*, the daughter wrote *Frankenstein*. Who were they?

The Play's the Thing

Odd that the British, generally believed – at least by foreigners – to be a reserved, undemonstrative race, should have such a splendid theatrical tradition; and such a long one too, interrupted only in the nineteenth century when we went into a sudden and inexplicable decline, to be rescued at the end of it by Sir Arthur Pinero and George Bernard Shaw. Why did Dickens, with his passion for the theatre, never try his hand at serious playwriting? How marvellously he would have done it. . . .

1 Where is the only completely excavated Roman theatre in England?

2 What was the name of Shakespeare's wife? And, if you think that's too easy, what were the names of his three children?

3 Who wrote:
   a *The Spanish Tragedy?*
   b *The Revenger's Tragedy?*
   c *'Tis Pity She's a Whore?*
   d *A Mad World, My Masters?*

4 In which plays, by whom, would you find:
   a Lord Foppington?
   b Polly Peachum?

    c Tony Lumpkin?
    d Sir Joseph Surface?

5 Of what actor or actress was it said:
    a (By one of his leading ladies) 'Damn him,
       he could act a *grid-iron*'?
    b (By Hazlitt) 'To have seen her was an
       event in everyone's life'?
    c (By Hazlitt again) 'She ran upon the stage
       as a playground, and laughed from sincere
       wildness of delight. Her smile had the
       effect of sunshine . . . she rioted in her fine
       animal spirits'?
    d (By Coleridge) 'To see him act was like
       reading Shakespeare by flashes of
       lightning'?

6 Playing Sir Harry Wildair in *The Constant
Couple*, she remarked to James Quin in the
Green Room: 'In my conscience, I believe
half the men in the house take me for one of
their own sex.' Quin replied that he was sure
the other half could convince them to the
contrary. She is also said to have been the
only woman member of the Beefsteak Club,
and possibly even its President. Who was
she?

7 What actor or actress is particularly assoc-
iated with:
    a *The Bells*?
    b *The Only Way*?
    c *St Joan*?
    d Lady Bracknell in *The Importance of Being
       Earnest*?

8 *a* A leading actor-manager was half-brother
to a leading dramatic critic;
b A leading actress in her day was great-
aunt to a leading actor in ours.
Who are the people concerned?

9 Shakespeare and Dryden both wrote
tragedies on the same subject. What is the
name of Dryden's version?

10   Her appearance was magnificent: long
plaits of deep red hair fell from under a
purple veil over a robe of green upon
which iridescent wings of beetles glittered
like emeralds, and a great wine-coloured
cloak, gold embroidery swept from her
shoulders. (W. Graham-Robertson)
Seeing this vision, Oscar Wilde remarked:
'Judging from the banquet, Lady Macbeth
seems an economical housekeeper and
evidently patronises local industries for her
husband's clothes and the servants' liveries,
but she takes care to do all her own shopping
in Byzantium.' Who was the actress, and
who painted the celebrated portrait of her in
this costume, now in the Tate Gallery?

Hotch Potch

A final miscellany to round off the book, covering as wide a water-front as possible. Good luck – and thanks for sticking it out. . . .

1 Who was William Webb Ellis and for what was he renowned?

2 In July 1588 an English fleet destroyed the Spanish Armada.
   a Who commanded the English fleet?
   b What, in Spanish eyes, was especially significant about him?
   c Who commanded the Armada?
   d On what grounds did he beg to be relieved of his command?

3 For what did the village of Eyam, Derbyshire, earn the nation's gratitude?

4 What items of sporting equipment are said to have been employed in the fifteenth century to demonstrate the contempt of one European prince for another?

5 What do the following events have in common?
   a The first meeting of Queen Elizabeth and Mary Queen of Scots
   b Queen Victoria's state visit to Rome in 1882

 Answers on page 126

c The marriage of the Prime Minister, A. J. Balfour, in 1906

6 What was the King's Evil? And who was the last monarch to touch for it?

7 Who said, and of what occasion: 'I did think I did see all heaven before me, and the great God himself'?

8 Launched in 1843, the first propeller-driven ship to make regular Atlantic crossings, badly damaged in 1886 rounding Cape Horn, she spent eighty-three years rusting in the Falkland Islands. What is her name, who built her, and where is she now?

9 The death of which foreign prince, fighting with the British Army in the Zulu war, led to the court-martial of his brother-officer on a charge of cowardice?

10 Of what battle of the Second World War did Winston Churchill say: 'This is not the end. It is not even the beginning of the end. But it is, perhaps, the end of the beginning.'?

Answers

From the Horse's Mouth

1 *a* Lord Grey of Fallodon at the outbreak of the
    First World War
  b Lady Eden at the time of the Suez Crisis, 1956

2 Queen Mary, consort of George v. In September
  1939 Queen Mary moved to the country – a novel
  experience for her. She surprised the Duchess of
  Beaufort with this lack of familiarity with country
  matters.

3 *a* George iv, on first meeting his future Queen,
    Caroline of Brunswick
  b George ii, when his Queen, Caroline of
    Ansbach, suggested on her deathbed that he
    marry again
  c George i

4 Nurse Edith Cavell (1866–1915)

5 Broadcast on the radio during the Second World
  War, these lines gave the French Resistance
  warning of the date of the invasion of Normandy.

6 *a* Oliver Cromwell, in a letter to the Church of
    Scotland on 3 August, 1650
  b Robert Clive, in a reply during a parliamentary
    cross-examination in 1773. He described how,
    after the Battle of Plassey, all the richest men in
    India had vied for his favour, spreading out
    their treasures for his taking.
  c Captain R. F. Scott at the South Pole, 1912.

7 *a* Henry Ford
  b Thomas Carlyle

    c Henry James
    d Thomas Hardy

8 The Walcheren Expedition of 1809, when Chatham and Strachan were sent to the island to destroy the French fleet in the Scheldt. They were so dilatory that nothing was achieved but the capture of Flushing.

9 Queen Caroline, in 1820. Quoted in the diary of Lord Colchester.

10 George II; Anne the Princess Royal; The Prince of Orange

Oddly Enough

1 Anne Boleyn had a rudimentary extra finger on one hand.

2 He hadn't got one. 'He gott a terrible clap of a Black handsome wench that lay in Axe-yard, Westminster . . . which cost him his Nose, with which unlucky mischance many witts were too cruelly bold. . . .' (Aubrey's *Brief Lives*)

3 It started a war. On 9 April 1731 an English sailor, Robert Jenkins, reputedly had an ear cut off by a Spanish captain off Havana, Cuba. The incident provided the immediate cause of hostilities and led to the War of Jenkins Ear.

4 It would, she said, be found to have 'Calais' engraved on it when she died.

5 He is said to have been crowned aged nine months with his mother's bracelet.

6 His estranged wife, Queen Caroline, was forbidden admittance to the Abbey.

7 Berengaria of Navarre, Richard I's wife, never set foot in England. (He was seldom there himself.)

8 Eleanor of Aquitaine had formerly been the wife of Louis VII and, therefore, Queen of France.

9 It had only nineteen days Britain then adopted the Gregorian Calendar, which was eleven days in advance of the Julian; 3–13 September were therefore omitted.

10 It took place in a railway carriage at Compiègne in France.

The Death of Kings

1 Richard II, in *Richard II,* Act III, Scene ii

2 *a* Edward II
   b Richard I
   c Edward V

3 Edward V and Edward VIII

4 *a* 'Remember' (To Bishop Juxon, reported in Rushworth's *Historical Collections,* 1701.)
   b According to Macaulay, Charles II's last words were that he 'had been a most unconscionable time dying: but he hoped they would excuse it'. (Alternatively, according to Burnet, 'Let not poor Nelly starve.')
   c 'How is the Empire?' (reported in *The Times*) or, according to an unsubstantiated story, when

Queen Mary promised him that they would soon return to Bognor for convalescence, 'Bugger Bognor.'

5   *a* Queen Elizabeth I
    b Queen Victoria

6 Henry II. Of his sons, Henry died – in the course of a revolt against his father – of a fever at Martel; Richard (who succeeded to the throne as Richard I) died of a crossbow wound at Châlus in the Limousin; John died during his flight of 1216 when his kingdom seemed to be reduced to the litter on which he was borne.

7 George IV

8 Jane Seymour, Henry VIII and Edward VI

9 Henry IV. It was prophesied that he would die in Jerusalem; he actually died in the Jerusalem Chamber of Westminster Abbey.

10 Richard III at Bosworth, 22 August 1485

Not Upon Oath . . .

1 Henry VIII said this of Anne of Cleves, whose portrait had been painted by Holbein.

2 The infant Jane Austen ('The History of England') of Edward IV

3 The Rev. Sydney Smith of William Pitt the Younger

4 J. M. W. Turner of Thomas Girtin (1775–1802)

5 Disraeli of Gladstone

6 Daniel O'Connell of Sir Robert Peel

7 Sir Walter Raleigh of Henry VIII

8 Thomas Babington Macaulay of James I

9 The Earl of Chatham of Oliver Cromwell

10 John Ruskin wrote this on the death of Charles Dickens.

The Missing Link

1 All committed suicide.

2 The name of Fox. Charles James Fox (1749–1806); George Fox, founder of the Society of Friends, (1624–1690); John Fox (or Foxe), author of *History of the Acts and Monuments of the Church*, popularly known as *Foxe's Book of Martyrs*, 1563.

3 They were the only English kings since the Norman Conquest to die unmarried.

4 They were all Kentish rebels: Wat Tyler led the Peasants' Revolt of 1381, Thomas Wyatt led a rebellion of Kentish men against Mary I's proposed marriage to Philip II of Spain in 1554, Jack Cade led a rebellion of Kentish gentry against high taxes and alleged corruption during Henry VI's reign of 1450.

5 All were forts of 'the Saxon Shore' during the Roman occupation of Britain.

6 All were Queen Victoria's grandchildren.

7 All were English: Richard of Cornwall, son of King John (1209–72); Nicholas Breakspear of St Albans (1100–59); the eldest daughter of Queen Victoria (1840–1901).

8 *a* All are London churches by Sir Christopher Wren: St Stephen, Walbrook; St Swithun, Cannon Street; St Vedast, Foster Lane; St Bride's, Fleet Street.

  b All are London churches by Nicholas Hawksmoor: St George, Bloomsbury; St Alphege, Greenwich; St Mary, Woolnoth.

9 All were Prime Ministers. Lord Salisbury formed governments in 1885, 1886 and 1895, Lord Derby in 1852 and 1866, the Duke of Newcastle in 1754 and 1757, the Earl of Liverpool in 1812.

10 All were the scenes of so-called mutinies. (The Curragh, 1914, was not really one, though nor-

mally so described.) The Nore and Spithead were
in 1797, Invergordon in 1931.

Gunpowder, Treason
And Plot

1 *a* In 1678 a fictitious plot, implicating among
others the Duke of York, was invented by Titus
Oates, who alleged that the Catholics were
about to massacre the Protestants, burn
London and assassinate Charles II. Some thirty
innocent people were executed.

b In 1605 Robert Catesby, Thomas Tresham,
Guy Fawkes and other Roman Catholics were
accused of plotting to blow up King James I and
Parliament during the State Opening on 5
November.

c This was a conspiracy in 1683 to seize or kill
Charles II and his brother James on their way
from Newmarket near Rye House Farm,
Hoddesdon, Herts. The King left earlier than
planned, however, and the plot miscarried. Its
discovery led to the execution of Lord William
Russell and Algernon Sidney, and the flight
abroad of the Duke of Monmouth and Lord
Grey.

2 Sir Roger Casement, executed for high treason
because of his support for the Sinn Fein rebellion

3 *a* A letter, alleged to be written by Cominturn
chairman G. E. Zinoviev, that was circulated
before the 1924 General Election inciting
British Communists to sedition.

b The letters supposedly written by Mary Queen
of Scots to Lord Bothwell, at least one of which
was held to prove the complicity of the Queen
in the murder of her husband, Darnley. They

were kept in a casket which fell into the hands of the Earl of Morton in 1567.

Masham: the others all gave their names to plots against Elizabeth 1 on behalf of Mary Queen of Scots.

Operation Bernhard

a Hereward the Wake

b Henry, 1st Lord Percy of Alnwick, father of Harry Hotspur

c The Duke of Monmouth

Lambert Simnel

Cato. The Cato Street Conspiracy was a plot, in 1820, by a group of revolutionaries to murder members of the Cabinet while at dinner and set up a republic.

The Mutiny on the Bounty in 1789

The Pilgrimage of Grace; its leader was Robert Aske.

Any Other Name

a Henry 1 (because he was literate)

b John

c William 11 (from his red hair)

d Charles 11 (from his favourite racehorse)

e William 1v

f William 1 (in Normandy)

g Henry 11 (from his short tunic)

h Edward 1

Queen Anne and Sarah, Duchess of Marlborough

The British Expeditionary Force of 1914. The Kaiser had referred to them as 'contemptible' and they adopted the name.

a Edward 1

b Sir William Wallace (1270–1305)

5 They were all used by Sir Winston Churchill, (*a*) in his wartime correspondence with President Roosevelt, (*b*) when submitting paintings to the Royal Academy, (*c*) for security reasons when travelling during the Second World War.

6 Queen Elizabeth I. 'Eyes' was the Earl of Leicester, 'Spirit' Sir Walter Raleigh, 'Lids' was Sir Christopher Hatton, 'Frog' was the Duc d'Alençon.

7 *a* Lord Ismay
   b Lord Mountbatten
   c Professor Lindemann, later Lord Cherwell
   d General Sir Henry Maitland-Wilson
   e Lord Auchinleck

8 *a* Joan, Countess of Salisbury, wife of the Black Prince
   b Margaret, daughter of Eric II and Margaret of Norway. When her grandfather Alexander III of Scotland died in 1285 she was acknowledged Queen of Scotland and betrothed to Edward, son of Edward I of England, but died on her way from Norway.
   c Joan of Arc, so called because of her heroism at the siege of the town in 1429

9 *a* George Villiers, Duke of Buckingham. The name was given him by James I – the allusion is to *Acts* vi, 15 where those who looked on Stephen the Martyr 'saw his face as it had been the face of an angel'.
   b Henry Dundas, first Lord Melville (1740–1811), was so called by Walpole, because when the Opposition denounced the Bill for restraining trade and commerce with the New England colonies on the ground it would cause a famine, he said that he was 'afraid' the Bill would not have this effect.
   c Charles, 2nd Viscount Townshend (1674–1733). On retirement from politics in 1730 he

devoted himself to agricultural pursuits.

d Catherine Howard, fifth wife of Henry VIII
ceeded him as Protector in 1658 but proved
utterly incapable and abdicated the following
year. He spent the next twenty years abroad,
but returned to England about 1680 and lived
on until 1712.

a The evacuation from Dunkirk in 1940
b Hitler's proposed invasion of England in 1940
c The Allied invasion of France in 1944

Out of Wedlock

a Edward IV
b Edward III; She is supposed to have robbed him
on his deathbed.
c George I
d Catherine Howard, fifth wife of Henry VIII
e Edward VII
f Charles II
g George II

2 William IV; the actress was Dorothy Jordan and
their children were called FitzClarence.

3 'Fair Rosamond' – Rosamond Clifford, mistress
of Henry II

4 Edward II and Piers Gaveston

5 Buccleuch (Lucy Walter); Grafton (Barbara Villiers); Richmond (Louise de Kéroualle); St
Albans (Nell Gwynne)

6 Cora Pearl

7 Lewes. George Eliot (Mary Anne Evans) lived
with George Henry Lewes from 1854 to 1878. In
1880 she married J. W. Cross.

8 *a* John Keats
b Lord Byron
c Percy Bysshe Shelley

9 Ellen Terry, E. W. Godwin, Edward Gordon Craig and Isadora Duncan

10 Herbert Henry Asquith and Venetia Stanley (who married Edwin Montagu); David Lloyd George and Frances Stevenson

Art and Architecture

1 *a* Sir Joseph Paxton (1801–1865)
  b Sir John Vanbrugh. Born in 1664, his first known architectural drawings are those made for Castle Howard in 1699.
  c Inigo Jones (1573–1652)
  d Sir Christopher Wren (1632–1723)

2 *a* Sir Giles Gilbert Scott
  b Sir Basil Spence
  c J. L. Pearson
  d Sir Denys Lasdun
  e Sir Christopher Wren
  f William Wilkins
  g Sir Edwin Lutyens
  h Sir Alfred Waterhouse
  i Sir William Chambers

3 *a* Uppark, West Sussex
  b Stratfield Saye House, Hampshire, and Apsley House, London
  c Blenheim Palace, Oxfordshire
  d Hughenden Manor, Buckinghamshire
  e Clouds Hill, Dorset

4 *a* Thomas Gainsborough
  b William Powell Frith
  c Sir James Thornhill
  d William Hogarth
  e Ford Madox Brown

5 *a* Norfolk
  b Suffolk and Essex

c Warwickshire
d Yorkshire

Thomas Gainsborough

John Ruskin of James McNeill Whistler. Whistler
sued him for libel and won a farthing's damages,
without costs.

This is a painting on two panels, now in the
National Gallery, depicting King Richard II being
presented to the Virgin and Child by his patron
saints.

Sir Joshua Reynolds

John Julius Angerstein; Sir Henry Layard; Sir
Hugh Lane

The Black, the Bloody and
the Rest

Sir William Douglas, Scottish chieftain, who
died in 1392
6 December, 1745, when news reached London
that the Young Pretender had entered Derby
The relic of the True Cross left to Scotland by
St Margaret in 1093, which was captured by
the English at the battle of Neville's Cross in
1346

A riot in Trafalgar Square on 13 November
1887, which started as a demonstration by the
unemployed. The police moved in and one
demonstrator was killed.

The assizes after the Monmouth Rebellion of
1685 when Judge Jeffreys sentenced 150 rebels
to death and 800 to transportation.

The last Scandinavian king of York, d. 954

The first major action of the American War of

Independence, which took place outside Boston on 17 June, 1775.

b A battle fought on 14 September, 1402, after the English under Hotspur cut off a Scots raiding force under Douglas.

c A battle of 1333 against the Scots, won by Edward III and fought to set Edward de Balliol on the Scottish throne.

4 a Riots in 1780, led by Lord George Gordon, to compel the House of Commons to repeal the bill passed in 1778 for the relief of Roman Catholics.

b Protests in 1839 and 1843 against the Turnpike Trusts. Men dressed as women destroyed toll-gates. The reference is to the departure of Rebecca from her father's house in Genesis xxiv, 60: 'Let thy seed possess the gate of those that hate them.'

5 a A Parliament summoned by Charles II (8 May 1661–24. January 1679); so called because of the numerous pensions granted to the King's supporters.

b The Parliament assembled at Edinburgh, 1 January 1661, of which it is said the members were almost perpetually drunk.

c The Parliament that lasted twelve years and five months, from 2 November 1640 to 20 April, 1653 and then continued (after the expulsion of the Rump) until 1660.

d The 'Parliament' convened by Cromwell (who had no authority to summon real parliaments) in 1653. It was named after one of its leading members, a fanatic called Praise-God Barebones.

6 a A fund for the benefit of poor clergymen and the building of parsonages

b A common name for *anthriscus silvestris* – cowparsley

c A gesture – thumb to nose and fingers spread

a An Act of 1913 empowering the Home Secretary to release suffragettes on hunger strike when their health was endangered and to re-arrest them on recovery

b Passed in 1774 in retaliation for the Boston Tea Party, they included closing the Port of Boston and quartering troops in the town.

c An Act of 1665 prohibiting ministers ejected by the Act of Uniformity (which enforced the use of the Book of Common Prayer) from coming within five miles of their former parishes or of any town or city

a A hangman and executioner of the later seventeenth century. He numbered among his victims the Duke of Monmouth and Lord Russell, an accomplice in the Rye House Plot.

b One of the leaders of the Peasants' Revolt, 1381

c Jack Horner is traditionally said to have been the Steward of the Abbot of Glastonbury who, during the Dissolution of the Monasteries, sent Henry VIII the title deeds of twelve manors concealed in a pie. Horner removed that of the manor of Mells, where the Horners have lived ever since.

a The Empress Matilda, daughter of Henry I and wife of the German Emperor, Henry V. the title of *Domina Anglorum* was officially conferred on her by the Council of Winchester in 1114.

b In Arthurian legend, Vivien, mistress of Merlin; in Scott's poem, Ellen Douglas of Loch Katrine.

c Florence Nightingale.

This was the name given to one of Charles II's Ministries (1670), after the initial letters of its members: Clifford, Ashley, Buckingham, Arlington and Lauderdale.

Dumb Friends

1 Sorrel was William III's horse. It stumbled by catching its foot in a mole hole, an accident which ultimately caused the King's death. 'The little gentleman in black velvet', i.e., the mole, was a favourite Jacobite toast celebrating this event.

2 The Rat, i.e., Ratcliff; the Cat, i.e., Catesby; Lovel the Dog, i.e., Francis, Viscount Lovel, known as the King's Spaniel. All were supporters of Richard III, whose crest was a hog or boar.

3 *a* Diamond
  b Mathe. It deserted the King and attached itself to Bolingbroke.
  c Flush
  d Dash

4 *a* Samuel Johnson's cat
  b A huge elephant weighing six-and-a-half tons, that gave rides to thousands of children at the London Zoo during the latter half of the nineteenth century. He was later sold to Barnum's circus in America and died after being hit by a train in 1886.

5 *a* Richard II
  b Richard III
  c Henry VIII
  d The Earl of Warwick

6 *a* Copenhagen, the Duke of Wellington's horse
  b Boatswain, Byron's dog

7 Volonel, Lord Roberts's horse which had carried him from Kabul to Kandahar in the victorious march of 1886. It was awarded the Afghan war medals by special order of Queen Victoria and on its death, aged twenty-seven, was buried in the grounds of Royal Hospital, Chelsea.

8 *a* Mary Queen of Scots

b Dick Turpin

c Warwick the Kingmaker

d Richard III

e Richard II

Frederick, Prince of Wales. Alexander Pope wrote the verse.

They were the three stallions from which, in the early eighteenth century, the English thorough-bred was developed.

The Great Wen

It was the lowest point where the Thames could be bridged or forded.

a Hyde Park Corner (Richard Belt)

b Paddington Green (L. Chavalliaud)

c Victoria Embankment at Westminster Bridge (Thos. Thornycroft)

d Waterloo Place (Arthur Walker)

e Kensington Gardens (W. Calder Marshall)

f New Embankment Gardens (W. H. Thorny-croft)

a A seventeenth-century Secretary to the Treasury, Sir George Downing

b Henry Jermyn, Earl of St Albans, a great friend of Queen Henrietta Maria

c The Italian merchants or bankers from Lombardy who set up here in the Middle Ages and exercised a monopoly in pawnbroking till the reign of Queen Elizabeth I

d The game of Palle Malle, in which a round ball was struck with a mallet through a high arch of iron. It was fashionable in the reign of Charles II, who used to play it here with his court.

e Named after a 'Piccadilly Hall' situated nearby early in the seventeenth century. It was the

       home of a retired tailor who had made money
       from *pickadils*, the edging of ruffs, etc.

4 *a* The Lord Mayor of London, Sir Thomas
       Bludworth
   b Samuel Pepys

5 St John's, Smith Square

6 *a* William Morris, in *The Earthly Paradise*
   b Noel Coward, in 'London Pride'
   c Francis Thompson, in 'The Kingdom of God'

7 *a* A scavenger in sewers
   b An unloader of timber from ships
   c A beachcomber on the river-front at low tide

8 Maida Vale (The Battle of Maida)

9 *a* The author of *Survey of London*, 1598, the first
       book of its kind and the principal authority for
       our knowledge of Tudor London
   b The landlord of the King's Head, Gray's Inn,
       and author of *The London Spy*
   c Property developer, builder and designer of
       much of Belgravia
   d A fashionable London brothel-keeper

10 *a* Sam Weller (*The Pickwick Papers* by Charles
       Dickens)
   b 'A man who is tired of London is tired of life'
       (Samuel Johnson)

Murder Most Foul

1 *a* William II, in the New Forest
   b George Villiers, Duke of Buckingham, at
       Portsmouth
   c Spencer Perceval, who became Prime Minister
       in 1809 and remained in office till 11 May 1812
       when Bellingham, a bankrupt broker from
       Liverpool, shot him dead as he entered the
       lobby of the House of Commons.

Prostitutes – from the attentions of Jack the Ripper

His Danish captors killed him at a feast with left-over bones.

The murder of Thomas à Becket in Canterbury Cathedral

a John George Haigh, executed 6 August 1949

b William Palmer, 1824–56

c The Rev. James Hackman. He claimed that he had only wanted to kill himself, before her eyes, but that he had been suddenly seized by an irresistible impulse. Dr Johnson maintained that as he had two pistols this was untrue; Boswell attended the trial.

William Burke and William Hare made their living in early nineteenth-century Edinburgh by killing people and selling their bodies to Dr Knox, of 10, Surgeon's Square, for medical research. Singly or together, they despatched over a dozen victims. Burke was hanged; Hare turned King's evidence and ended his life as a beggar outside the British Museum; Dr Knox was not even called as a witness.

a That of Doreen Marshall by Neville Heath in July 1946

b The multiple murders committed by John R. H. Christie, who killed at least six women, including his wife, between 1939 and his arrest in 1953

c That of Eileen 'Gay' Gibson, an actress, on the high seas in 1947, the body being pushed out through a porthole. A ship's steward, James Camb, was charged and found guilty; he escaped hanging because a Criminal Justice Bill – which would have abolished the death penalty – was then under discussion in Parliament, and was released from prison in 1959.

8 Crippen and his mistress, Ethel Le Neve, fled to Canada on the ss *Montrose*, where they aroused suspicion – particularly Miss Le Neve, who was dressed as a boy. The captain sent a wireless message to London, and Chief Inspector Dew of Scotland Yard was waiting for them when they reached Quebec. It was the first time that wireless was used in a murder hunt.

9 The leader of a gang of deported Latvian anarchists who were disturbed by the police while raiding a jeweller's shop in Houndsditch on 16 December 1910. In the ensuing fight three policemen were killed. On 2 January 1911 two of the gang were found at 100, Sidney Street, Mile End Road, which was surrounded. Winston Churchill, then Home Secretary, characteristically hurried down to watch. The house caught fire during the siege; one of the wanted men was shot, the other asphyxiated.

10 Lord Frederick Cavendish, who had been sworn in the same morning as Chief Secretary for Ireland, was set upon and murdered, together with his under-secretary, T. H. Burke.

The Inner Man

1 *a* Captain Cook was killed by natives in Hawaii (the Sandwich Islands) in 1779.
   b There is a story that he knighted it 'Sir Loin'. Fuller in his *Church History* says: 'Dining with the Abbot of Reading, he (Henry VIII) ate so heartily of a loin of beef that the abbot said he would give 1,000 marks for such a stomach. "Done" said the king and he kept the abbot a prisoner in the tower, won his 1,000 marks and knighted the beef.'

  c His last words are said to have been 'I think I
    could eat one of Bellamy's pork pies.'

2 Alexis Soyer

3 *a* Henry I
  b King John
  c George, Duke of Clarence, younger brother of
    Richard III, who was drowned in one.

4 It refers to Queen Anne, who was very fond of
brandy. It was written by a wit on her statue in
front of St Paul's Cathedral, just opposite a 'gin-
palace' on Ludgate Hill.

5 *a* The 1st Lifeguards, before the Peninsular War
  b The 11th Hussars, from their cherry-coloured
    breeches

6 This was a mixture of cauliflower, potatoes,
onions, swedes, carrots and oatmeal, covered by a
pastry or potato crust, which was recommended
by the Ministry of Food (under Lord Woolton) as
a means of eking out scarce rations in the Second
World War.

7 The 4th Earl of Sandwich (1718–92). He was a
compulsive gambler who without stopping playing would eat a piece of meat between two slices of
bread, thus introducing the idea of the sandwich.

8 Geoffrey Chaucer in *The Canterbury Tales* (in a
modern version by Neville Coghill)

9 Samuel Johnson

10 The introduction of tea into England from
Holland is attributed to him.

Odds and Ends

1 'Charing' is a corruption of '*chère reine*', the
beloved Queen Eleanor of Castile, wife of Edward
I. Her body was brought from Harby, Notts. to
Westminster for burial, and a cross was erected

at each place where it rested. Charing Cross marks the last of these.

2 *a* Gregory 'the Great', on seeing little fair-haired boys in a slave market and being told that they were Angles, is said to have remarked: '*Non Angli sed Angeli*' – 'Not Angles but Angels.'

b William the Conqueror slipped and fell when disembarking at Pevensey. He quickly seized a handful of earth, and raised it above his head as a sign that England should be his.

c The birth of the future King Edward IV. His father, Henry VI, had become insane only a few weeks before.

d The retreat of the British Army from Kabul, 1842. Of some 700 Europeans and 3,800 Indian soldiers who left Kabul on 6 January, one only – Surgeon Brydon of the Army Medical Corps – reached Jelalabad a week later.

3 The intervention of Miss Emily Davison, a suffragette, who flung herself in front of the King's horse, Anmer, as it was rounding Tattenham Corner. Horse and jockey suffered only slight injuries; Miss Davison died later in hospital. (She had not intended suicide: the unused half of her return ticket to Northumber was found afterwards in her handbag.)

4 *a* the Roman invasion of Britain under Julius Caesar, 55–54 BC

b The completion of his *Historia Ecclesiastica Gentis Anglorum, 731 AD*

c The proclamation of Henry I's daughter Matilda as Queen in 1141, after the capture of King Stephen at Lincoln

5 Oddly enough, on board HMS *Dragon* at Sierra Leone, on 5 September 1607, for the entertainment of Portuguese and English guests.

6 *a* Sir Walter Raleigh

b King Alfred

7 *a* 'Four and twenty blackbirds baked in a pye' is a reference to Henry James Pye, Poet Laureate in 1790, who wrote an extremely flatulent ode to George III full of allusions to 'feathered choirs'.

b The Great Plague of 1665, the symptoms of which were a rose-pink rash, and (later) compulsive sneezing. People carried posies of herbs in an attempt to ward off the infection.

c She was Patience, daughter of Dr Thomas Muffet (d. 1604), the famous entomologist 'whose admiration for spiders has never been surpassed'.

8 It was the name under which lawn tennis was first introduced in 1874. It comes from the Greek word for ball-playing.

9 Gangs of street bullies who terrorized London between the Restoration and the reign of George I

10 Edward the Confessor, on 6 January 1066 – nine days after the Abbey was consecrated

Eye-Witness

1 The opening of the Great Exhibition in 1851; from Queen Victoria's diary

2 The funeral of George II in 1760, as described by Horace Walpole

3 The arrival of Napoleon at HMS *Bellerophon* off Rochefort in 1815, from the account of Midshipman George Hume

4 The execution of Charles I, from Andrew Marvell's 'Horatian Ode upon Cromwell's Return from Ireland'

5 The murder of David Rizzio, 1565, from the *Narrative* of Lord Ruthven, one of the Scottish nobility involved in the deed

6 The Black Hole of Calcutta, 1756, from the account of J. Z. Holwell, one of the few to survive the ordeal

7 John Donne poses for his memorial. The result is now in St Paul's Cathedral. From Aubrey's *Brief Lives*

8 The coronation of George IV in 1821, as described by Benjamin Robert Haydon.

9 John Evelyn, on Charles II

10 The Battle of Trafalgar, 1815. Letter written by a sailor on HMS *Royal Sovereign*

Once More Into the Breach

1 On 22 February 1797 some 1,400 convicts and galley slaves landed in Pembrokeshire from Republican France. They were led by an American. No sympathetic Welsh rising having taken place, they were rounded up, hopelessly drunk, in a few days. The British took especial pleasure in sending them back to France, as valuable *citoyens*, with the next batch of exchanged prisoners.

2 *a* Edward III (1356)
 b George II (1746)
 c William and Mary (1689)
 d Henry VIII (1513)
 e Stephen (1138)
 f Henry III (1265)
 g James II (1685)

3 The Duke of Wellington

4 *a* The Battle of Crécy; the longbow
 b The first Battle of the Marne, 1914
 c The Battle of Prestonpans

5 *c* Harold of England defeated Harold Hardrada

of Norway for the English throne, which the former then lost to William of Normandy.

6 *a* George II as Dettingen in 1743; he won.
   b Prince Albert (later George VI) at the Battle of Jutland, 1916.
   c Winston Churchill, about the charge at Omdurman in 1898 in which he took part

7 *a* The name given to a large gun from the works of Bertha Krupp in the First World War
   b A V1 Flying Bomb in the Second World War
   c A floating harbour used for the invasion of France in 1944
   d Nicknames for the first two prototype British tanks in the First World War

8 *a* Agincourt, 1415 (From Shakespeare, *Henry V*)
   b Bosworth, 1485 (From Shakespeare, *Richard III*)
   c Blenheim, 1704 (From 'The Battle of Blenheim' by Robert Southey).
   d Waterloo, 1815 (From Byron's 'The Eve of Waterloo')
   e Balaclava, 1854 (From 'The Charge of the Light Brigade' by Alfred, Lord Tennyson)

9 The Battle of the Falkland Islands

10 *a* Agincourt
   b Trafalgar
   c Bosworth
   d Blenheim
   e Naseby
   f Waterloo

Done to Death

1 Sir Walter Raleigh

2 Laurence, 4th Earl Ferrers, b. 1720. According to *Burke's Peerage*, 'although not bereft of intellect, this nobleman frequently evinced strong symptoms of a constitutional violence of temper; and in one of the paroxysms of rage habitual to him, His Lordship put to death his own confidential land-steward, an aged gentleman of the name of Johnson, in January 1760, for which offence he was condemned to suffer death and was executed accordingly at Tyburn 5 May following.'

3 Lord Lovat in 1747

4 Boiling to death

5 *a* James, Marquis of Montrose, 1612–1650
   b Chidiock Tichbourne, who was hanged in 1586 for his participation in the Babington plot in favour of Mary Queen of Scots against Elizabeth

6 *a* Mary Queen of Scots
   b Two: Anne Boleyn and Catherine Howard

7 Sir Thomas More

8 Samuel Pepys. Harrison was one of the regicides who signed Charles I's death warrant and was executed after the Restoration.

9 To Tyburn, where all three highwaymen were hanged. Maclaine, the son of a Scottish minister, held up (among many others) Horace Walpole, to whom he subsequently sent a letter of apology; as Walpole put it, 'the whole affair was conducted with the greatest good breeding on both sides'. When he was taken, half White's Club went to call on him in prison. Du Vall, the 1670s' answer to Errol Flynn, was given a memorial service by his many admirers at St Paul's, Covent Garden, and an epitaph beginning:
   Here lies Du Vall; reader, if Male thou art,
   Look to they purse; if Female to they heart.
William Parsons was the Duchess of Northumberland's nephew and, so far as is known, his profession's only Old Etonian.

0 *a* High Treason

   b Nine days, from 9 to 18 July, 1553

   c Edward VI had died without issue, and she was Henry VIII's great-niece.

   d Sixteen

The Printed Word

1 The Book of Common Prayer

2 *a* Tacitus, *Agricola*

   b The Venerable Bede, *Ecclesiastical History*

   c Julius Caesar, *Gallic Wars*

3 *a* Edward Gibbon, *The Decline and Fall of the Roman Empire*

   b Winston Churchill, *A History of the English-Speaking Peoples*

4 *1066 and All That* by Walter Sellars and Robert Yeatman

5 TO THE ONLIE BEGETTER OF THESE INSUING SONNETS MR. W. H.

6 *The Dictes or Sayengis of the Philosophres*; Caxton, 1477

7 (*c*) 1621; (*e*) 1623; (*d*) 1643; (*b*) 1651; (*a*) 1678

8 An eighth-century illuminated manuscript of the Four Gospels, the finest existing example of Irish monastic penmanship

9 It was written during his imprisonment in the Tower of London, and was subsequently banned for being 'too saucy in censuring the acts of kings'.

0 An immensely popular book of royalist propaganda which appeared only ten days after the execution of Charles I, describing itself as *The Portraiture of His Sacred Majesty in His Solitudes and Sufferings*. It was written by Francis Gauden, later Bishop of Ely.

The Body Politic

1 *a* Sir Charles Barry and A. W. N. Pugin
   b The Old Palace had been burnt down in 1834.
   c May 1941
   d Oxford

2 Karl Marx, as European correspondent of *The New York Tribune*, 12 April 1853

3 No MP may resign, but if he accepts an office of profit under the Crown he is disqualified from membership of Parliament; it has therefore been customary since 1740 to apply for this office as a way of resigning a parliamentary seat.

4 *a* Melbourne and Palmerston
   b Churchill and Eden
   c Salisbury and Balfour

5 *b*

6 Benjamin Disraeli wrote *Vivian Grey*, *The Infernal Marriage* and *Ixion in Heaven*. Winston Churchill wrote *Savrola*.

7 The Churchills: Randolph, Winston, Randolph, Winston

8 In the same order as in the question: (*a*) 1829, (*b*) 1832, (*c*) 1834, (*d*) 1851

9 John Milton, 'for the Liberty of Unlicensed Printing'. 'Give me', he wrote, 'the liberty to know, to utter and to argue freely, according to conscience, above all liberties.'

10 Lord Salisbury who was Prime Minister from 1885–6, 1886–92 and 1895–1902. (The Earl of Home, before he renounced his peerage to become Sir Alec Douglas-Home, sat there for a few days in 1963.)

A Chapter of Accidents

1 *a* He was killed by a fall from a horse in 1087.

b He was killed in a carriage accident on the Marlborough Downs in 1813.

c He was run over by the train at the inauguration of the Manchester and Liverpool Railway, 15 September, 1830.

d Both were killed by falls from scaffolding in the cathedrals where they were working as architects: William at Canterbury, Basevi at Ely.

2 The South Sea Bubble; the last line reads 'South Sea at best a mighty bubble'.

3 They indicate the survival rate for the different classes of ticket-holders on the *Titanic*.

4 *a* Sir Richard Grenville's lone stand in the Azores, 1591

b Sunk by the *Bismarck* in 1941

c Sank in view of Henry VIII in 1545

d Sank near Barfleur with Henry I's only son, William, on board, 1120

e Sunk by the Japanese in Singapore harbour, 10 December 1941

5 The last earthquake in London

6 Francis Bacon, Viscount St Albans

7 The Tay Bridge disaster. The bridge, which had been open only since the previous year, collapsed in a gale just as the Edinburgh-Dundee express was passing over it.

> It must have been an awful sight,
> To witness in the dusky moonlight,
> While the Storm Fiend did laugh, and angry did bray,
> Along the Railway Bridges of the Silvery Tay . . .

8 General Wladyslaw Sikorski was the leader, Rolf Hochhuth the playwright, and the play – *Soldiers*.

9 A manoeuvre ordered by the Commander-in-Chief, Mediterranean, Vice-Admiral Sir George Tryon, to form his fleet into two columns and reverse direction by turning inwards. Despite reminders from his officers that for this to be practicable the minimum distance between the columns must be eight cables, Tryon insisted that it should be only six. As a result HMS *Victoria* was rammed by the leader of the other column, HMS *Camperdown*, and sank almost at once, with the loss of 358 men – including Tryon himself.

10 The airship R101

Glad Rags

1 Charles I. He was afraid that if he was cold he would shiver and people would think it was from fear.

2   *a* The Duke of Wellington

    b The 7th Earl of Cardigan, who led the Light Brigade in the charge at Balaclava. It appears to have been first worn in the bitterly cold Crimean winter.

    c Lord Raglan, the British commander in the Crimean War, who first wore the 'Raglan' coat.

3 All are forms of helmets.

4 William of Orange. 'When the King of England (Charles II) suggested that he might care to take them off, he replied that since he and his wife would have to live together for a long time, she would have to get used to his habits; he was accustomed to wearing his woollens and he had no intention of changing now.' (Letter from Liselotte, Duchess of Orleans, 11 January, 1678.)

5 Mrs Amelia Jenks Bloomer

6 Bombast was padding – called Spanish Bombast because the fashion originated in Spain. Bombasting reached its limits in the grotesque peasecod-belly – a stuffed-out hump overhanging the girdle in front – worn by dandies between 1575 and 1595.

Samuel Pepys, in his Diary for 1669. The Queen was Catherine of Braganza.

A farthingale was a petticoat held out with graduated hoops, fashionable between 1550 and 1590, and the prototype of the later crinoline.

King John

Dandies of the 1770s, given to exaggerated forms of dress, with high-piled wigs. They were a boon to contemporary caricaturists.

Dust To Dust

1   *a* Caen
    b St Germain
    c Hanover

2   *a* Dylan Thomas
    b W. H. Auden
    c T. S. Eliot
    d Lord Byron

3 This is an anonymous suggested epitaph for Frederick, Prince of Wales. His father was George II.

4 Captain L. E. G. Oates (1880–1912), a member of Scott's ill-fated expedition to the South Pole. This epitaph is inscribed on the cross marking the approximate place of his death. Being crippled with frostbite, he walked to his death in a blizzard to avoid being a burden to his companions.

5 Worcester Cathedral; it is the tomb of King John.

6   *a* Nowhere, he was buried at sea in 1596.
    b The Protestant Cemetery in Rome
    c Golders Green Cemetery
    d The island of Skyros, Greece

7 *a* An obelisk in Kensington Gardens
   b An Arab tent, carved in stone, at Mortlake
   c An outsize bust in Highgate

8 Ben Jonson. John Aubrey writes: 'He lies buried in the north aisle in the path of square stone . . . opposite to the Scutcheon of Robertus de Ros, with this Inscription only on him, in a pavement square of blew marble, about 14 inches square, O RARE BENN JOHNSON which was donne at the charge of Jack Young, afterwards knighted, who walking there when the grave was covering, gave the fellow eighteen pence to cut it.'

9 *a* Sir Christopher Wren in St Paul's Cathedral
   b Sir John Vanbrugh (by Abel Evans)
   c W. S. Gilbert (by Anthony Hope)

10 William Shakespeare's, at Stratford-upon-Avon:
GOOD FREND FOR IESUS SAKE FORBEARE
TO DIGG THE DUST ENCLOASED HEARE;
BLESTE BE YE MAN YT. SPARES THES STONES
AND CURST BE HE YT. MOVES MY BONES.

Servants of God

1 George Fox. His journal says that in 1651 the Lord told him to walk to Lichfield, and a mile outside to take off his shoes. When he entered the town 'the word of the Lord came unto me again to cry "Woe unto the bloody city of Lichfield"; so I went up and down the streets crying "Woe unto the bloody city of Lichfield". . . .'

2 *a* Religious reformers, followers of John Wycliffe
   b Supporters of the anti-Calvinist doctrines of Jacob Arminius (1560–1609), a Dutch theologian
   c A group which seceded from the Methodists in 1797

3 *a* Cardinal Wolsey
  b Bishop Hugh Latimer
  c Mother Julian of Norwich

4 John Bunyan; Bedford; *The Pilgrim's Progress*

5 (*a*) and (*iii*); (*b*) and (*iv*); (*c*) and (*v*); (*d*) and (*i*);
  (*e*) and (*ii*); (*f*) and (*vii*); (*g*) and (*vi*)

6 *a* He was burnt.
  b He was racked and hanged.
  c She was crushed, or pressed, to death.

7 Joanna Southcott (1750–1814)

8 *a* So called because the word *not* is omitted in the
    seventh commandment, making it 'Thou shalt
    commit adultery'. Printed in London by Barker
    and Lucas, 1632.
  b The Geneva Bible of 1560 was popularly so
    called because Gen. iii, 7, was rendered: 'The
    eyes of them bothe were opened and they sowed
    figge tree leaves together and made them
    breeches'. (The Authorized Version has
    'aprons'.)
  c Coverdale's Bible of 1535 is so called because
    Psalms, xci 5, is translated: 'Thou shalt not
    nede to be afrayed for eny bugges by night.'
  d The third edition (second folio) of the Bishops'
    Bible published in 1572 is so called because
    the decoration to the initial at the *Epistle to the
    Hebrews* is an incongruous woodcut of Jupiter
    visiting Leda in the guise of a swan. It came
    from an edition of Ovid's *Metamorphoses*.
  e A popular name for the Bishops' Bible of 1568
    because in it, Jer. viii, 22, reads: 'Is there no
    tryacle in Gilead, is there no phisition there?'

9 The lines refer to the destruction of the Shrine of
  Walsingham in Norfolk by Henry VIII.

10 *a* The Irvingites were followers of Edward Irving
    (1792–1834), a Scottish minister of magnetic
    personality. In 1830 he was excommunicated
    by the London presbytery for his tract on *The*

Orthodox and Catholic Doctrine of our Lord's Human Nature but continued to minister. In 1832 he was removed from his church at Regent Square when revivalist disturbances – including speaking in tongues – occurred there. His followers then constituted themselves the 'Catholic Apostolic Church'. Their principal place of worship in Gordon Square no longer exists, but there is still a large red-brick church by J. L. Pearson in Maida Avenue, W2.

b A sect founded *c.* 1651 by Ludowicke Muggleton (1609–98) and his cousin, John Reeve (1608–58), who claimed to be the 'two witnesses' of Rev. ii, 3–6. Though small, the sect continued until at least 1868.

c Also called the 'Plumstead Peculiars', they were a small sect of faith-healers founded in London in 1838, who, on the basis of Jas. v, 14, rejected medical aid.

Psst... Have you heard?

1 In Kenya. It was brought into prominence when the Earl of Erroll was murdered in 1941 just outside Nairobi.

2 Tranby Croft was an English country house in which, during a house party in 1891, Sir William Gordon-Cumming was accused of cheating at cards. The Prince of Wales – later Edward VII – a fellow-guest, was obliged to give evidence at the subsequent trial.

4 Oscar Wilde

5 Sir Roger Tichborne, lost at sea in 1854. In 1874 Castro was sentenced to fourteen years' hard labour for perjury.

6 He was the celebrated Rector of Stiffkey in

Norfolk, who was defrocked in 1932 for wildly promiscuous behaviour. Later he took to exhibiting himself in a barrel at holiday resorts. He was killed in 1937 by a lion, in whose cage he was appearing at Skegness.

7 The Hon. Unity Mitford

8 Sir Charles Dilke (1843–1911). His sister-in-law's sister, Mrs Donald Crawford, said that he had been her lover.

9 Frederick Augustus, Prince of Wales, the second son of George III. The lady was Mary Anne Clarke. His monument is the column in Waterloo Place above the steps leading down to the Mall.

10 Mary (Perdita) Robinson (1758–1800)

New Frontiers

1   *a* James Brindley (1716–1772) has been called the father of canals in Britain.

  b John Harrison (1693–1776) invented the Marine Chronometer for which he was awarded a £20,000 prize.

  c Dr J. Collis Browne was the inventor of 'Chlorodyne', a patent medicine used throughout the nineteenth and for most of the twentieth century, until it fell victim to food and drugs legislation.

  d Sir Frank Whittle was chiefly responsible for the jet propulsion aircraft engine. The first aeroplane to fly with a Whittle engine was the Gloster E28/29 on 14 May 1941.

  e Edward Jenner (1749–1823) invented vaccination against smallpox.

2 Sir William Herschel (1738–1822)

3 *a* Sir Humphry Davy
 b James Watt
 c Henry Cort
 d Sir Christopher Cockerell
 e Sir Barnes Wallis

4 The Hon. Robert Boyle, physicist and chemist

5 John Metcalf (1717–1810), stone blind from the age of six, musician, jockey, horse-dealer, soldier and smuggler, who surveyed and constructed some 180 miles of roads and bridges across the north of England.

6 *a* (iii) The Flying Shuttle
 b (iii) The Spinning Jenny

7 George Hudson (1800–1871) was given the name because of his success in promoting the building and amalgamation of railways. By the end of 1848 he controlled 1,450 out of 5,007 miles of line open in the United Kingdom, and his railway empire extended from Berwick-on-Tweed to London and from Yarmouth to Bristol. By 1865, however, he was bankrupt and imprisoned for debt.

8 *a* The mutiny led by Fletcher Christian against Captain William Bligh in 1787. The aim of the journey was to collect breadfruit from the South Seas in the hopes of introducing it to the British West Indies.
 b Captain James Cook, sent to the Pacific to observe the Transit of Venus on 3 June 1769
 c Charles Darwin and his scientific survey of South America
 d Captain Scott and his quest for the South Pole, 1911–12
 e Sir John Franklin, searching for the North West Passage in 1847
 f Sir Ernest Shackleton and his attempt to cross Antarctica in 1914–16. His ship was crushed in the ice, and the attempt failed; but he and his men all returned safely.

9 Joseph Priestley the chemist, who discovered oxygen in the 1780s

10 The Birmingham Lunar Society was formed *c.* 1760 by Matthew Boulton, Erasmus Darwin and John Whitehurst as a forum for the discussion of scientific ideas and inventions. Its monthly meetings were timed to coincide with the full moon so that members could travel home safely. Other members included Joseph Watt and Josiah Wedgwood.

The White Man's Burden

1 *a* Sir Charles Brooke, 'White Rajah' of Sarawak
   b Sir Thomas Stamford Raffles
   c Cecil Rhodes
   d Lord Lugard

2 *a* Nyasaland
   b Bechuanaland
   c Tanganyika and Zanzibar
   d The Gold Coast

3 Benjamin Disraeli

4 In the Victoria and Albert Museum, London. It is a working model of a tiger eating an Englishman. Tipu Sultan died fighting the British at Seringapatna (Seringapatam) in 1799.

5 To the transporation of convicts to New South Wales, Australia. The practice was suspended in 1840.

6 The Hudson's Bay Company

7 General Sir Garnet Wolseley (later Field Marshal Lord Wolseley), 1833–1913. 'All Sir Garnet' in army slang came to mean 'everything just as it should be'.

8 The Suez Canal. In 1875 the British Government bought the Khedive of Egypt's 177,646 shares in the Compagnie Universelle du Canal Maritime for £3,976,852. This gave them a 40% commercial share and, eventually, complete military control.

9 General Charles Gordon. He was killed by the Mahdi's soldiers at Khartoum on 26 January 1885, three days before a British relief expedition arrived.

10 Cecil Rhodes paid this sum to buy out independent prospectors at the Big Hole diamond mine, Kimberley, South Africa.

Spare Rib

1 John Knox (Title of a religious pamphlet, 1558)

2 *a* Lady Astor, in 1919
   b Elizabeth Garrett Anderson, in 1866

3 Florence Nightingale, on her arrival in the Crimea

4 *a* The daughter of the lighthouse-keeper on the Farne Islands, on 7 September 1838 she rowed with her father to rescue the survivors of the wreck of the *Forfarshire* steamboat.
   b Helping British soldiers to escape from Belgium in the First World War, for which she was executed by firing squad
   c Her work with the French Resistance in the Second World War

5 Lady Hester Stanhope, by Bedouin tribes in 1813

6 *a* The Byrons. Augusta was Lord Byron's half-sister, Augusta Ada his daughter, Annabella his wife, Allegra his illegitimate daughter.
   b The Brontës. All three were sisters.

c The Pankhursts. Emmeline Pankhurst was the mother of Sylvia, Christabel and Adela. Emmeline, Christabel and Sylvia were three of the most active supporters of the British movement for women's suffrage.

Dame Ethel Smyth (1858–1944)

a Edward IV married Elizabeth Woodville; Henry VII married Elizabeth of York; George VI married Elizabeth Bowes-Lyon.

b Henry VIII married Anne Boleyn and Anne of Cleves; Richard II married Anne of Bohemia; Richard III married Anne of Warwick; James I married Anne of Denmark. (James II's first wife Anne Hyde died before his accession.)
before his accession.)

c Henry VIII married Catherine of Aragon, Catherine Howard, and Catherine Parr; Henry V married Catherine of Valois; Charles II married Catherine of Braganza.

Mary Seaton, Mary Beaton, Mary Fleming and Mary Livingstone, all ladies in waiting to Mary Queen of Scots. (The Mary Carmichael mentioned in the Ballad was not included.)

Mary Wollstonecraft, and her daughter Mary Godwin (who married the poet Shelley)

The Play's the Thing

Verulamium (St Albans)

Anne Hathaway; Susanna, Hamnet and Judith

a Thomas Kyd
b Cyril Tourneur
c John Ford
d Thomas Middleton

4 *a* *The Relapse*, by Sir John Vanbrugh
  b *The Beggar's Opera*, by John Gay
  c *She Stoops to Conquer*, by Oliver Goldsmith
  d *School for Scandal*, by Richard Brinsley Sheridan

5 *a* David Garrick
  b Sarah Siddons
  c Dorothy Jordan
  d Edmund Kean

6 Peg Woffington

7 *a* Sir Henry Irving
  b Sir John Martin-Harvey
  c Dame Sybil Thorndike
  d Dame Edith Evans

8 *a* Sir Herbert Beerbohm Tree and Sir Max Beerbohm
  b Dame Ellen Terry and Sir John Gielgud

9 *All For Love* (Another version of the story of Antony and Cleopatra)

10 Ellen Terry, and John Singer Sargent

Hotch Potch

1 The question is best answered by a stone tablet set in a wall at Rugby School:

This stone commemorates the exploit of William Webb Ellis, who, with a fine disregard for the rules of football as played in his time, first took the ball in his arms and ran with it, thus originating the distinctive feature of the rugby game. AD 1823.

2 *a* Lord Howard of Effingham
  b He was a Roman Catholic, thus putting an end to King Philip's hopes that all English Catholics would rise to back his projected invasion.

   c The Duke of Medina Sidonia

   d That he possessed 'neither aptitude nor ability, health nor fortune', that he had no experience of war on land or sea and that he suffered from sea-sickness

3 When the Great Plague broke out in Eyam in September 1665 the entire village, led by its vicar, William Mompesson, placed itself in voluntary quarantine, with no one allowed to leave and no stranger allowed to enter. Virtually the whole population perished, but the disease spread no further.

4 Tennis balls, sent by the Dauphin to Henry v. (See Shakespeare's *Henry V*, Act I, Sc. ii.)

5 They never occurred.

6 Scrofula, which (according to popular belief) the royal touch could cure. The last ruling sovereign to make a regular practice of touching was Queen Anne, who touched the infant Samuel Johnson in 1712 – though Prince Charles Edward ('Bonnie Prince Charlie') is known to have done so in Scotland in 1745.

7 George Frederick Handel, of his state of mind while he was writing the *Messiah*

8 The *Great Britain*; Isambard Kingdom Brunel; in a special dry-dock in Bristol

9 The Prince Imperial, son of Napoleon iii and the Empress Eugénie. When he and Captain J. B. Carey were surprised on 1 June 1879 by a band of Zulus, Carey was found guilty of having thought only of his own escape and of leaving the Prince to his fate. The finding of the court-martial was later reversed by Queen Victoria.

10 El Alamein, 1942

The author and publishers are most grateful to Mr Michael Trend for his valuable assistance.